Pumping Away

(And Other *Really* Cool Piping Options For Hydronic Systems)

KARNER MECHANICAL, Inc.
Post Office Box 66167
Albany, New York 12206
(518) 330-2566

Thank you for your business!

© 1994 by Dan Holohan

For the Associates
KELLY, MEGHAN, COLLEEN, ERIN

Young and strong and...beautiful!

KARNER MECHANICAL, Inc.
Post Office Box 66167
Albany, New York 12206
(518) 330-2566

Thank you for your business!

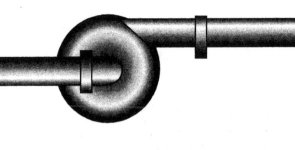

Pumping Away
(A *very* good idea)

"When did you first get the idea about 'the point of no pressure change?'" I asked.

*He turned from me and stared out the window for a long moment, and then he smiled a silly grin and said, "Oh, it's just something I've **always** known."*

"Oh," I echoed, like an empty canyon.

The Man Who *Always* Knew

When I knew Gil Carlson, he was never far from the cigarettes he so loved. On the days when I was fortunate enough to be able to sit and listen to this giant of the hydronics industry, it was always through a cloud of bluish smoke. I think the man used only one match a day.

The blue haze of those days seems almost poetic to me now. Gil was an engineer and he was brilliant. I was neither. Gil saw, I believe, the mechanics of hydronics in his mind's eye as Einstein must have seen the Universe. It all flowed together in a very visual way for him. It didn't for me.

But as a young man, I was lucky enough to have the chance to listen to him when he'd visit from Bell & Gossett's Illinois plant. Gil was B&G's Director of Technical Services for many years. He traveled the country and lectured to large groups of engineers about things hydronic.

When he'd come to New York, I'd sit in the smoke and attempt to see what he saw. I'd stare into the depths of my confusion and try to imagine the mechanical movements he described by way of charts and formulas as **real** things. I knew *he* saw them, but try as I might, I couldn't. Not at the time, anyway. On most days, I'd walk to the subway in total confusion and frustration.

I remember one January day when the wind blew cold in Manhattan and we sat together in an office perched high above Fifth Avenue. We drank hot coffee. Gil was a quiet man who rarely spoke unless asked a question. I struggled to find one that wouldn't reveal *too* much of my ignorance.

Finally, and more to break the silence than for any other reason, I asked him how he'd come up with this idea that the location of the circulator matters in a closed hydronic system. I knew that this principle, which Gil had proposed in an early-1960s paper, had radically changed the way professional engineers design hydronic systems. It's one of the cornerstones of hydronic heating, but it had never occurred to me to ask him this question before.

"When did you first get the idea about 'the point of no pressure change?'" I asked.

He turned from me and stared out the window for a long moment, and then he smiled a silly grin and said, "Oh, it's just something I've **always** known."

"Oh," I echoed, like an empty canyon.

Of course, his answer struck me as pretty bizarre. The principle was obviously something he'd arrived at along the way, but apparently, he'd realized it so long ago that he couldn't remember ever **not** knowing it.

"You mean you figured it out so long ago that you don't remember when?" I asked.

He smiled that silly grin again. "No," he said, "I've just **always** known."

"But why did you write the paper when you did?" I persisted.

He took a long drag on his cigarette and exhaled, adding to the thick haze that already filled the room. "I wrote the paper **then**, because that's when **they** asked me about it." He looked at me as though I should have known that. "You see," he continued, "I **always** knew about it, but they just never **asked** me before. That's why I wrote the paper when I did. Because they **asked** me." He smiled that Carlson grin.

"Uh huh," I said. "I see," I said. I let my empty head bob up and down. "I understand."

But, of course, I didn't. I'll tell you this, though. The moment burned itself into my memory, and as I think back on it now, I remember this neat quote I read somewhere: *"Talent is what you possess; genius is what possesses **you**."*

Gil Carlson *always* knew...but no one ever asked him about it before.

Which is why we should *all* ask more questions. You never know who might be waiting with a few answers.

"Pumping Away" (The way things used to be)

You can learn a lot by reading the old books and manufacturer's mildewed literature from days gone by. For instance, I came across this old catalog from the United States Radiator Corporation recently. Pretty nostalgic, isn't it?

This is a picture of one of the first "packaged" boilers. The boiler came with the burner and the circulator pre-mounted and wired so the installer could save time on the job.

Notice where the circulator is? It's on the supply side, "pumping away" from the boiler and the compression tank.

In the early days of hydronic heating, many boiler manufacturers did things this way. They found the circulator worked very well on the supply side of the system. They weren't quite sure why, but you have to remember that at the time, the science of forced hot water heating was still very young. The industry was learning more from experience than from scientific research. They were, more or less, making up the rules as they went along.

After the War

When the GIs came home from World War II, America went on the move. President Eisenhower signed a bill into law that began the massive project of linking us together through a system of interstate highways. That law quickly changed the way we lived because the highways led to suburbs, and suburbs led to the American dream of home ownership.

Before the War, most Americans lived in cities or out in the country. Either steam heat or coal stoves warmed those who lived in the cities. The folks in the country had stoves, too, as well as fireplaces and, in some cases, gravity furnaces. A fortunate minority had central steam, or gravity hot water heat. Most of those folks were pretty well-to-do.

In 1946, space heaters that burned either coal or wood heated nearly half of all the buildings in America. The other half of America was divided almost equally between hot air furnaces (both the forced-air and gravity type), and boilers (both steam and hot water).

The building boom that followed World War II changed all this. Most tract-housing builders were interested in keeping their selling price as low as possible. Naturally, they favored furnaces. Furnaces have always been cheaper than boilers.

The steam and hot water people watched as their market share steadily dropped. In 1946, boilers heated 22% of all the homes in America (today, boilers heat about 6%). Hydronic equipment manufacturers offered what they believed to be a more comfortable and more healthful system, but their going-in price *was* high. In the years following the war, they found it increasingly difficult to get the builders of low-priced tract homes interested in hydronics.

To get the price down, they began to design their systems around higher-temperature water. Higher design temperatures allowed them to use smaller pipes, valves, fittings and radiators. But as they upped the ante with temperature, a nagging problem popped up. The mechanical seals in the circulators they were using at the time couldn't take the high-limit temperatures of those redesigned systems. When the pump seal failed, it leaked water back into the bearing assembly and created a no-heat call.

To get around the problem, installers began to pipe the circulator on the return side of the system where the water was coolest. This helped a great deal and before long, most installers got into the habit of piping their circulators on the return side of every job.

Boiler manufacturers followed the installers' lead and moved their circulators to the return side of their "packaged" boilers as well. The pumps seemed to work well in that position, and it made everyone happy.

Habit took over, and the return side soon became the "right" side as far as everyone was concerned.

Big-Time Problems

Before long, *all* the pumps were going in on the return side of the system. It didn't matter how big the building was. The idea was to expose the pump to only the coolest water in the system.

Naturally, larger buildings called for larger pumps, and these, too, went in on the return side of the system where the water was coolest. Habit, fueled by success, ruled the day.

Back in those days, many design engineers liked to heat larger buildings with single-pipe, diverter-tee systems. Since the pressure drop of diverter tees is cumulative, the engineers usually wound up with relatively powerful, high-head pumps on the return side of their systems. The head pressures of these pumps frequently exceeded the system's static fill pressure.

During the 1950s, many of these larger jobs began to fall prey to oxygen corrosion problems. Boiler tubes would rot out, cast-iron boiler sections would suddenly develop huge holes. Pump seals and bearing assemblies would fail and systems would air-bind to such an extent that radiator bleeding became a daily activity.

And no one knew what had gone wrong.

Except Gil Carlson, of course. That's when he wrote his famous paper. Engineers across the country read it and realized that they were causing their own problems by putting those high-head pumps on the return side of the system. Gil explained that when you put a high-head pump on the return side of the system, **pumping toward** the compression tank, it may be capable of dropping its suction pressure to a point where the system pressure becomes sub-atmospheric. When that happens, you get a partial vacuum at the inlet of the pump. Air will come rushing into the system through the automatic air vents, and any other place it can find. That's what was causing the rampant oxygen corrosion problems in all those systems.

Gil did such a good job of explaining that engineers immediately began to design their jobs with the pumps on the **supply side** of the boiler, "pumping away" from the compression tank. In this position, the pump couldn't drop its suction pressure into a sub-atmospheric state. In fact, just the opposite happens! When a pump is "pumping away" from the compression tank, it *raises* the overall system pressure by adding its discharge pressure to the system's static fill pressure.

The engineers moved the pumps and the problems went away.

Manufacturers of larger pumps, armed with this new knowledge, began to develop mechanical seals that could take higher water temperatures and last longer on the supply side of the boiler. Fortunately, high-tech ceramics were becoming available to the pumping industry as a result of the NASA space program. These ceramic seals could handle the higher supply-side temperatures without a problem. Pump manufacturers embraced them.

Nowadays, *all* hydronic heating pumps can take at least 225 degree F. water. This includes the small, water-lubricated circulators boiler manufacturers use on modern packaged boilers. These little pumps don't have mechanical seals, but manufacturers still build them to take hotter-than-normal water (typically 230 degrees, Fahrenheit).

Temperature isn't a problem anymore. But old habits sure die hard!

The Power of Habit

As all of this was evolving, boiler manufacturers moved the pumps to the return side of their packaged boilers - to be on the safe side. They realized pump manufacturers were using more and more high-tech ceramics, but at that point, they didn't see much reason to change the location of the pump.

Habit had taken over.

Not that it really mattered much in those days. The little pumps boiler manufacturers were using on packaged boilers didn't produce enough "head" pressure to cause the problems many engineers were seeing on those larger jobs. The pumps on the packaged boilers ran on 1750-rpm motors and produced, at most, only about three pounds of head pressure. Since residential systems operated on at least 12 psi static fill pressure, there was no chance a little circulator could drop its suction pressure below atmospheric and suck in air through the automatic vents.

So with little reason to change, boiler manufacturers left the little pumps right where they were - on the return side of the system. It seemed like a good and safe place to put them, and it certainly made packaging easier. With the circulator down low on the return side of the boiler, the crate didn't have to as strong as it would have to be if the pump were up on top. It didn't have to be as high either. That meant they could stack more packaged boilers on a truck and in a warehouse. Wholesalers liked that too.

Installers were used to having the pumps on the returns. All the manufacturers' literature showed the pumps on the return. Everyone was used to doing it that way. There didn't seem to be any reason to change.

Until now that is.

The Point of No Pressure Change

"The Point of No Pressure Change." That's what Gil Carlson called the place in a closed hydronic system where the compression tank connects into the system distribution piping. "The point of no pressure change" is the one place in the system where the pump can't affect the overall system pressure. You can measure "The Point" with a pressure gauge, but the only way you can *see* it is to use your imagination.

Let me give you the key points right up front, and then I'll go back and explain why all these things happen:

→ First, if you pump *away* from the point of no pressure change, the pump will add its pressure to the system's static fill pressure.

→ However, if you pump *toward* the point

of no pressure change, the pump will not be able to raise the system pressure any higher than it already is.

➥ But, since it's a pump, it *has to* develop a difference in pressure if it's to move water.

➥ So, if it can't *raise* the system pressure it will do the only other thing it can do. It will *lower* its suction-side pressure to create the pressure differential it needs to move water.

➥ When that happens, you'll have problems.

Here are a couple of diagrams that should make this easier to visualize.

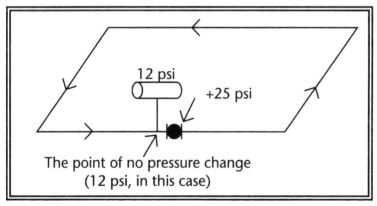

The point of no pressure change
(12 psi, in this case)

This is a simple loop of piping with just the major players: the pump and the compression tank. I've removed all the other components to make it as simple as possible. Okay, the place where the tank connects into the distribution piping is "the point of no pressure change." I have that point set at 12 psi, the system fill pressure. The pump, in this case, is a fairly large one. It can develop a head pressure of 30 feet, or put another way, about 13 psi (2.31 feet of head pressure equals 1 psi of pump pressure). My guess is this pump would probably have a 1 HP, 1,750-rpm motor.

Now, as you can see in the drawing, when you **pump away** from the compression tank (the point of no pressure change), your pump will add its 13 psi head pressure to the system's static fill pressure of 12 psi. That gives you a total pressure of 25 psi at the pump's discharge (12 psi static pressure, plus 13 psi head pressure).

Naturally, as soon as the pump comes on, water will begin to flow everywhere. And as it does, it gradually loses the pressure the pump developed. That's because when water flows through a pipe, it creates friction. The friction "wears down" the pump's head pressure. By the time it gets back to the compression tank, the only pressure left is the static fill pressure that was there when the pump was off. In this case, that's 12 psi.

❖

Always remember, the point where the tank connects to the distribution piping is the point of no pressure change. The pump *can't* affect the pressure at that point in *any* way.

❖

Okay, now let's move the pump to the other side of the compression tank.

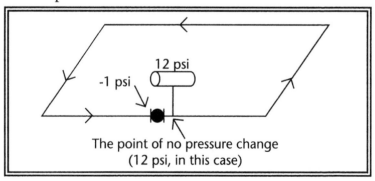

12 psi

-1 psi

The point of no pressure change
(12 psi, in this case)

Here, the pump *tries* to raise the system's static fill pressure above 12 psi, but it can't because, as you now know, the tank is the point of no pressure change. The pump, however, still needs to develop its differential head pressure, so it does the only thing it can do: **It drops its suction pressure by the full 13 psi it's capable of developing in this particular system.**

That leaves you with a *negative* 1 psi pressure at the suction side of the pump. Don't you just *hate it* when that happens?

The pump's suction pressure is now **below** atmospheric pressure. Air pours into the system through any opening it can find. The automatic air vents pop open and start sucking in air instead of venting it out. The stem packing on the valves near the pump does the same thing, so does the pump's mechanical seal.

What do you think all that fresh air is going to do to your system?

I'm not making this up, my friend. This is all **very** real, and it's why you'll **always** see large, commercial pumps "pumping away" from the compression tank.

And this, in a nutshell, is what Gil Carlson always knew.

Why The Pressure Can't Change

Now let me try to explain **why** all this happens the way it does.

Imagine you have a loop of piping with nothing but a pump and a compression tank. The tank can be a plain-steel type, or it can be a diaphragm-type tank. It really doesn't make a difference.

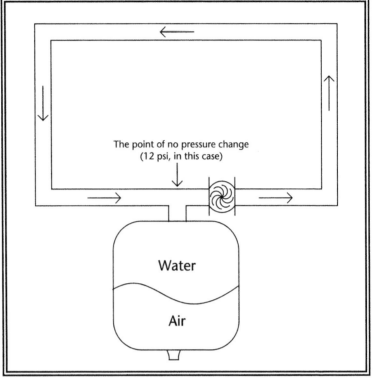

The point of no pressure change
(12 psi, in this case)

Water

Air

Okay, you filled the system with water until the static pressure reached 12 psi, as you would in a two-story house. The air in the compression tank will make sure the pressure remains on the system once you disconnect the hose you used to fill the system. The air in the tank acts as a "spring" to hold the pressure. You need that air cushion because water isn't compressible. Without a tank, the pressure would have dropped instantly when you disconnected the hose.

Now here's the key question I want you to consider:

When the circulator runs, can it add any water to what's already in the compression tank?

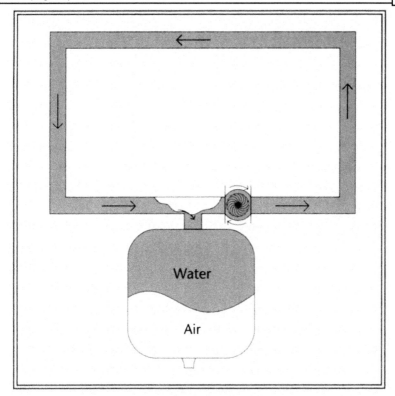

Now think carefully before answering. And remember you have only so much water to work with in this system. That means that if the pump puts water into the tank, you're going to be left with a big empty space in the water that's flowing through the system piping.

Can that happen? Do you think you can wind up with a few inches of nothingness in the pipe? That would be pretty weird, wouldn't it?

Oh, but maybe you think the space *won't* be empty. Maybe you think it will fill with air. Okay, I'll go along with that.

But where did the air *come* from?

It didn't come from the tank. It had no way of getting from the tank to the system piping. Besides, if you're using a diaphragm-type tank, as we are here, instead of a plain-steel tank, the air can't leap through the tank's diaphragm, can it?

And air can't suddenly appear out of nowhere, can it? Hmmmm, I don't think the system water can suddenly transform itself into air in some magical molecular way, do you?

So if you believe the pump put some of the water into the tank, you're now left with a bit of absolute nothingness in the water that's flowing through your system piping. There can be no other option if the water flowed down into the tank. You have several inches of outer space between two slugs of flowing water. Spooky, eh?

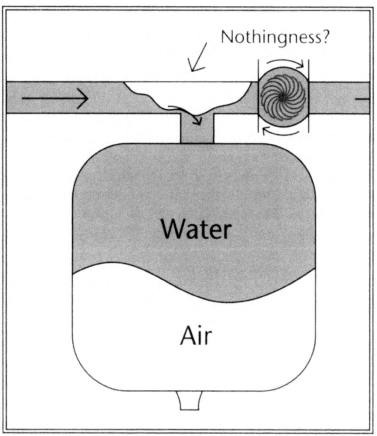

But don't you think that if that *were* the case, Mother Nature would instantly fill that empty space with the water that surrounds it.

Mother Nature **hates** a vacuum.

But wait a minute, for her to fill the gap, she'd have to use some of the water that's flowing around the loop, wouldn't she? And since there's only so much water to work with in the system, she'd have to stretch what's there to make it fill that empty space. Do you think she can do that? Can you stretch water as though it were taffy? Hmmmm.

Put that thought on the back burner for a minute and consider this now: The highest pressure a pump produces is at its discharge flange, and the lowest pressure it produces is at its suction flange.

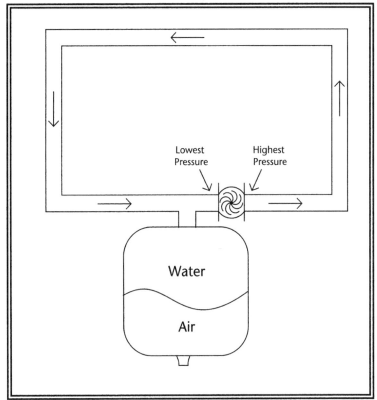

Since high pressure goes to low pressure, you would think the water that leaves the discharge of the pump would want to get back into the pump's suction as quickly as possible, wouldn't you? If you were water, would you make a 90-degree turn into the compression tank? I don't think *I* would. I think I'd go straight ahead. Wouldn't you?

High pressure goes to low pressure...always.

I think that when you come right down to it you have to conclude that when the pump runs, **not one single drop of water enters the compression tank**. It simply can't.

Accept that, and then carry it a step further.

When the pump moves water past the compression tank, can it suck water out of the tank?

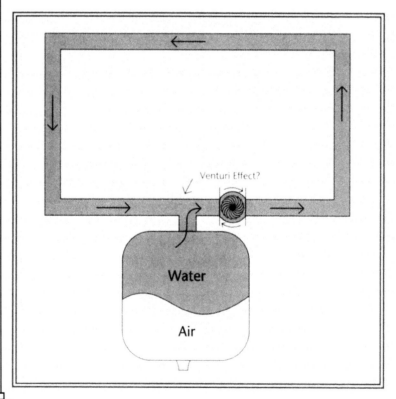

You know, in a sort of "venturi" way? Can it do that?

Think about it.

Okay, if you said yes, I now have to ask you a very important question: When the pump sucks the water out of the tank...where does it put it?

It can't put it into the piping loop because the piping loop is already completely filled with water. You can't add more water to something that's already filled, can you? Water's not compressible, is it?

No, there's no "venturi effect" going on here. The truth is the pump can't pull any water at all out of that tank, nor can it add any water *to* that tank.

And because it can do neither of these things, **it can't change the pressure at the point where the tank connects to the system.** That's because of a scientific fact established by an Englishman named Robert Boyle more than 300 years ago.

Boyle's Law of Perfect Gasses

Robert Boyle invented the vacuum pump and studied the effects of pressure on gasses. Scientists called his famous finding, *Boyle's Law of Perfect Gasses*. Simply put, Boyle's Law states that if have a gas trapped in a tank, its volume will shrink as you add pressure to it, and it will expand as you remove pressure from it. Boyle's Law assumes the temperature will stay the same during the experiment.

Nowadays, Boyle's Law may seem like common sense—squeeze a gas and the pressure rises, let it go, and the pressure falls—but back in the Seventeenth Century, this was a *major* scientific revelation. Robert Boyle showed people things they'd never seen before.

If you want to see a quick example of Boyle's Law today, open a plastic, two-liter bottle of soda and quickly turn it over. Watch carefully as the soda pours out; notice how the bottle caves in.

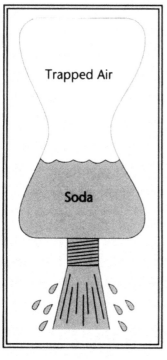

Trapped Air

Soda

The bottle caves in because when you turn the bottle over, a little bit of air gets trapped above the soda. The falling soda increases the space the air occupies and allows it to expand. Remember, air is not only compressible, it's also expandable.

As the trapped air expands, its pressure obeys Boyle's Law and drops below atmospheric. That's why the bottle collapses. The atmospheric pressure on the *outside* of the bottle exceeds the pressure on the *inside* of the bottle. Since high pressure will *always* go to low pressure, the bottle caves in. It's as simple as that.

Now, instead of a bottle of soda, imagine you have a plain-steel compression tank. Let's say it's filled halfway with water; the other half contains air. The only way you can increase the pressure of the air trapped inside the tank is to compress it, right? And to do that, you'd have to add more water to the tank, of course.

In a similar way, if you wanted to *decrease* the pressure of the air trapped inside the tank, you'd have to remove water *from* the tank - as you decreased the pressure of the air trapped in the soda bottle by removing soda *from* the bottle.

Which reminds me, have you ever seen what happens to a steel compression tank if you drain the system without allowing air up into the tank?

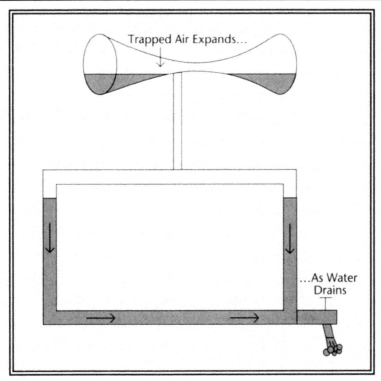

It collapses just like that soda bottle! Looks like somebody drove a truck over it, in fact. How come? Well, the air expanded to fill the space the falling water created. The high pressure on the outside went to the lower pressure on the inside and the tank wound up on the losing end. And don't you just hate it when *that* happens?

Unfortunately, your customer's not too interested in hearing about Boyle's Law at that point.

Here's the key point in all of this:

Since the pump can't add water to the tank or remove water from the tank, it can't change the air pressure in the tank by compressing it or expanding it.

That's why Gil Carlson called the place where the tank connects into the distribution piping, "the point of no pressure change."

He knew.

What *Can* Add Water To The Tank?

There are only two things that can add more water to a compression tank. First, there's the feed valve. Open it and you'll bring in more water from the outside. The additional water has to go into the tank because the rest of the system is already filled with water. When the water enters the tank, it squeezes the air and increases its pressure.

The other thing that can add water to the system is heat. If you heat water from, say, 40 to 180 degrees, Fahrenheit, you'll wind up with about five percent more water than you started with. The expanded water moves into the compression tank and squeezes the air, raising its pressure.

Under normal conditions, the pump can't open the feed valve or heat the water, so it can't add water to the tank in either of those two ways. And because it can't, the compression is in charge, it's **not** the other way around.

Every time it starts, the pump has to "ask" the compression tank what it's allowed to do with its differential pressure. The tank rules.

How Pumps Work In Closed Systems

We call the pumps we use in hydronic systems "circulators" because they don't lift water to the top of the system, they just, well, circulate it!

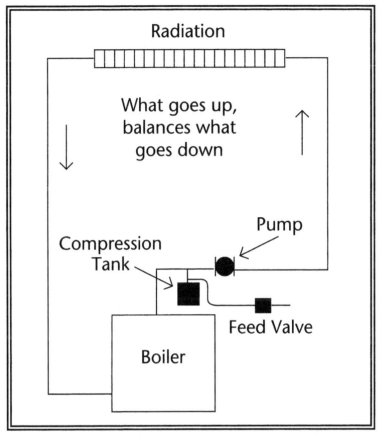

In a closed hydronic system, there's no need to lift water because the system's already filled to the top and pressurized. The pressure reducing valve takes care of that. All we're asking the circulator to do is to *turn* the water. In a closed hydronic system, the circulator acts very much like the motor on a ferris wheel. The weight of the water going up balances against the weight of the water coming down. There's no lifting, only turning.

Pump manufacturers call the force the circulator develops, "total dynamic head," or simply, "head," for short. Head represents the pump's ability to overcome the friction the water will create as it flows around the system. The pump operates on a "curve" such as this one.

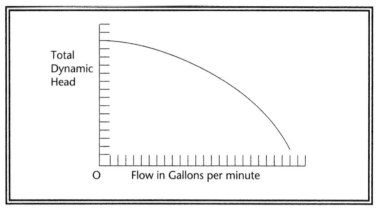

All pump manufacturers publish pump curves. The curve shows the relationship between flow rate (gallons per minute) and head pressure (the pump's ability to overcome resistance to flow). The more resistance there is in the piping system, the less flow you'll get, and vice versa.

It's easy to check a pump's performance. All you have to do is install a pressure gauge at the discharge of the pump and a compound (pressure and vacuum) gauge at the suction. Larger pumps have screwed tappings right in the flanges for this purpose.

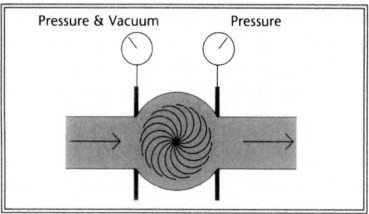

The discharge pressure will always be higher than

the suction pressure. That's the way the pump makes the water move. It takes the balanced pressure that exists in the system when the pump is off and upsets it. And because high pressure **must** go to low pressure, water flows around the system.

The pump creates this pressure differential by using an impeller to spin the water and create velocity. The water then has to leave the pump through a channel that's a bit smaller than the one it used to enter the pump.

Here's what the impeller looks like.

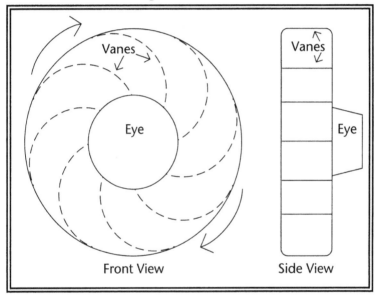

Front View   Side View

See the hole in the center? That's called the "eye" of the impeller. It's like the eye of a hurricane - the low pressure point at the center of a whirling centrifugal force.

When the pump starts, the impeller spins in a way that has its slanted vanes *slapping* the water, not digging into it. I mention this because, on larger, three-phase pumps, you can reverse the rotation by switching two wires. The pump *will* move water while operating in reverse rotation, but not very well, and this is definitely **not** good for the pump.

The impeller uses centrifugal force to throw the water from the eye to the outer edge of the impeller. An impeller is like one of those spinning rides at an amusement park. No matter where you're sitting when the ride starts, you quickly find yourself pressed tightly against the outer edge once it's up and running. Centrifugal force throws you away from the center, just like it throws the water out of the impeller.

In a pump, centrifugal force just has to move the little bit of water contained inside the pump body (the "volute") from the "eye" to the outlet. That's enough to unbalance the system's equilibrium and make every drop of water in the system move. And because water's not compressible, the pump moves the water *everywhere* at the same instant (except, of course, up and down the line connecting the compression tank to the distribution piping).

I mention this because it may not occur to you when you're standing in the room with the radiation. Water moves *everywhere* at the same time, but heat doesn't. And heat is what you're sensing when you're standing in that room. The heat can keep you from really understanding how pumps work.

Here's what I mean.

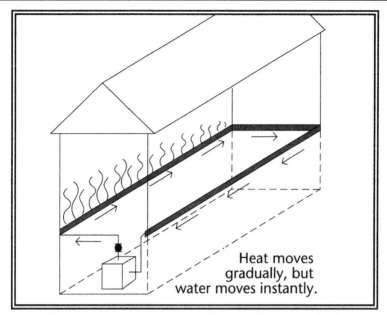

Heat moves gradually, but water moves instantly.

Let's say you're in a house heated by a single loop of copper fin-tube baseboard. When the circulator starts, all the water in the loop moves at the same instant, but some of that water is hot and some of it is cold. Because of this, your senses can fool you. You may believe the pump is pushing and pulling the water, when actually it's doing neither.

As you stand in the house, your sense of **touch** tells you this room over here is getting hot before that room over there. It's as though the pump is paying more attention to this room than to that room.

Now, as you listen to the baseboard expand, your sense of **hearing** tells you the same thing - the pump is acting on one room before another.

Watch the drapes ripple as the convective air currents rise out of the radiator enclosure. Your sense of **sight** tells you there's some sort of "Slinky Effect" going on here! The water seems to be pushing and pulling. Look at it! The pump sure seems to be acting on one side of the system before it gets to the other, doesn't it?

As you smell the melting crayons, which Junior deposited in the baseboard last summer, your sense of **smell** tells you things are definitely happening in a room-by-room way.

Let's see, what else? Taste! If you were to stick your tongue into the baseboard, your sense of **taste** would tell you there's definitely a "Slinky Effect" taking place here (even though there isn't).

Hey, it's enough to confuse *anyone*! All your senses are telling you the pump is "pulling and pushing" the water, but the fact is it's doing neither. It's **circulating** the water, and believe me, that makes a *big* difference.

You see, all the pump can do is throw out what's inside of itself, and when it does, **every single drop of water in the system moves at the exact same instant.** It's circulating, not pushing and pulling.

And when the water circulates, not one drop enters or leaves the compression tank. That's the important part. And that's why the tank is in charge of the pump's pressure differential.

Pump Pressure Differential

The pump has to produce a difference in pressure, but because it's a centrifugal pump, **it doesn't have to make its discharge pressure go up.** It can make water flow just as easily by dropping its suction pressure. Sounds strange, I know, but it's true.

It works like this. Let's say you have a small water-lubricated pump that can produce about a 6 psi difference in pressure (that's about 14 feet of head). The little pumps most boiler manufacturers use on their packaged boilers nowadays are more than capable of doing this.

Put that little pump on a system filled to 12 psi static pressure and it can produce its pressure differential in any number of ways, depending on its location in relation to the compression tank.

For instance, try butting the pump right up against the point of no pressure change and watch what happens when you pump away from the compression tank.

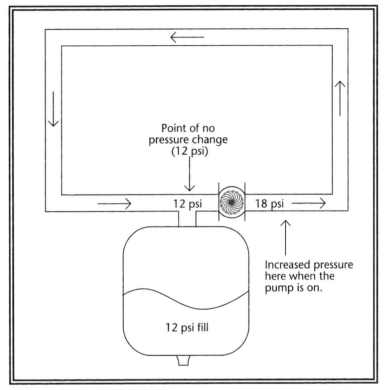

In this position, the pump will add its 6 psi differential pressure to the 12 psi static fill pressure that's already there. By creating differential pressure, the pump upsets the system's pressure equilibrium and creates flow *everywhere* - except, of course, in the line leading to the compression tank.

As you can see, you have 12 psi at the pump's suction and 18 psi at its discharge. All of the pump's differential pressure is showing up as an **increase** in system pressure. That's good!

Now let's move the pump halfway around the loop

and see what happens.

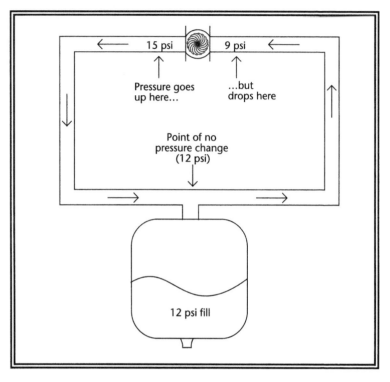

Because the point of no pressure change (the place that **must** remain at the 12 psi static fill pressure) is now halfway around the system, the pump is showing half of its pressure differential as an increase and the other half as a decrease. You now have a drop of 3 psi at the suction side of the pump, and an increase of 3 psi at its discharge.

Water flows *exactly* as it did in the last example because there's still a 6 psi pressure differential across the pump (15 psi - 9 psi = 6 psi differential).

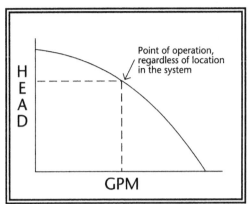

If you look at a pump curve for this particular pump, you'll see that it's moving the same amount of water whether it's situated right at the compression tank, or halfway around the system. The tank's location in relation to the pump doesn't affect the flow, **it only affects how the pressure differential appears across the pump.**

Okay, now I want you to move the pump right up to the point of no pressure change. Go ahead. Pump right at it.

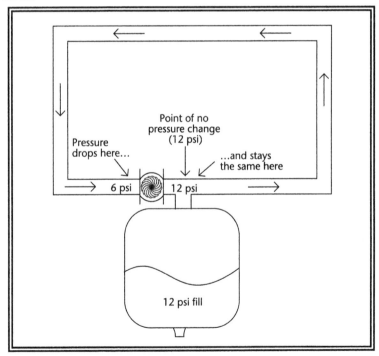

See? You still have your 6 psi differential across the pump. Even though it's only 12 psi, the discharge pressure is *still* higher than the suction pressure of 6 psi. Water flows as it did in the other two examples. You can see it right there on the pump curve. However, in this case, the pump shows its pressure differential **entirely** on its suction side because it can't make the pressure at the tank go any higher than 12 psi. That's the point of no pressure change!

But as long as the pump produces a difference in pressure from supply to return, water will flow.

Always remember, in a closed hydronic system, the pump doesn't have to show its pressure differential as an increase. It can just as easily show it as a decrease on the suction side and still make the water flow.

❖

Knowing this, you can now use the pump's pressure differential in a positive way to help you solve many of your air- and noise-related problems before they start. Watch.

Some Significant Science

And now we come to Mr. Henry, another long-dead scientist. Like Mr. Boyle, Mr. Henry also wrote a law, which he called...Henry's Law. Surprised?

Henry's Law belongs to the science of physical chemistry. It tells us that the weight of a gas dissolved in a fixed quantity of a liquid is directly proportional to the pressure of the gas on that liquid, at a constant temperature.

Quite a mouthful, isn't it? What it means is that the more you compress a gas, the more a liquid will be able to absorb it. You know that already, and that brings us back to that two-liter bottle of soda.

Soda bottlers add carbon-dioxide to soda to give it its distinctive fizz. Carbon-dioxide is a gas, just like oxygen and nitrogen and hydrogen. Soda will absorb carbon-dioxide into solution in direct proportion to the pressure inside the bottle.

Here, let's experiment a bit.

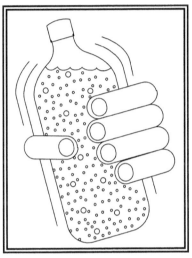

Grab that bottle and shake it until everyone around you screams and runs away!

Now you can concentrate. You see those thousands of carbon-dioxide bubbles coming out of solution and rising to the top of the bottle? Set the bottle down for a few minutes and watch as the bubbles quiet down and disappear. Where did they go?

If you look closely, you'll notice the bottle cap has popped up a bit.

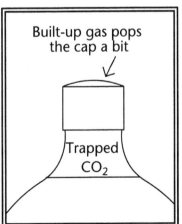

Built-up gas pops the cap a bit

Trapped CO_2

The carbon-dioxide you shook loose from the soda gathered at the top and is now pushing in all directions. That's why the cap is bowing out a bit. If you unscrew the cap, you'll get wet.

So do it!

But don't do it all the way. Just crack the seal enough to release the gas that's trapped under the cap. And when you do it, watch very closely because you're going to see something amazing. The soda will literally **explode** with bubbles. They'll appear out of nowhere!

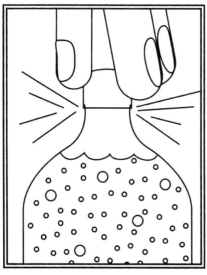

You know what's going on? When you released the pressure on the soda by popping the cap, thousands of tiny carbon-dioxide bubbles that had been absorbed in the soda came crashing out of solution because the pressure that held them in the liquid was no longer there.

The gas that appeared when you shook the bottle was almost immediately absorbed into the soda by the increased pressure that little "expansion tank" under the bottle cap created. The trapped gas pressed down on the soda in much the same way as a compression tank presses down on the water in a hydronic system. When you opened the cap, you released the pressure, and the gas came flying out of the liquid.

What you've just done is prove that Mr. Henry was right and that his law is good. Isn't science cool?

The Relevance To Heating

Now that you know that gasses such as carbon-dioxide and, yes, even ordinary air can be absorbed into a fluid in direct proportion to the system's pressure, I want you to think about what happens to the air in the system when the pump comes on.

For instance, consider what happens when a little pump, such as the one boiler manufacturers regularly use on their packaged units, starts. Let's say you install that little pump on the supply side of the boiler, pumping *away* from the compression tank.

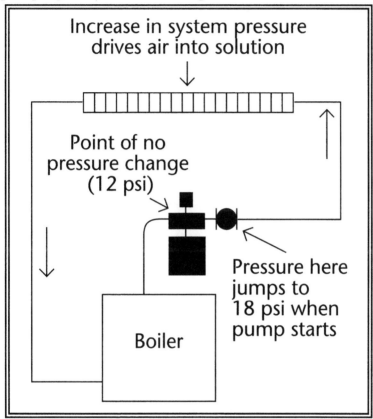

Increase in system pressure drives air into solution

Point of no pressure change (12 psi)

Pressure here jumps to 18 psi when pump starts

Boiler

The pump comes on and adds about 6 psi to the system's static pressure. The pressure throughout the system piping increases (except at the point of no pressure change, of course). That increase in pressure drives the air bubbles that gathered at the high points of the system into solution. The pump then moves the water, and the air it has absorbed, back to the boiler room and the air separator. The air separator removes the air from solution in one of several ways and spits it out.

The system runs air-free and quietly because the pump is helping to rid it of air - right from the very first time it starts up. You wind up with happier customers and fewer callbacks. Not bad, eh?

Now let's move the pump to the other side of the boiler and watch what happens.

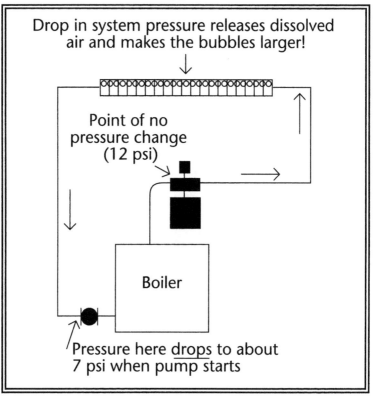

Drop in system pressure releases dissolved air and makes the bubbles larger!

Point of no pressure change (12 psi)

Boiler

Pressure here <u>drops</u> to about 7 psi when pump starts

You're now pumping right at the point of no pressure change so the pump has to drop its suction pressure. Let's say, in this case, the pump drops its suction pressure by about 5 psi, while increasing its discharge pressure by 1 psi. That slight increase would allow for the distance between the pump's discharge and the point of no pressure change (the compression tank).

The air that's trapped in the radiator has no chance of being absorbed into the water now. Just look at it!

Instead of increasing the system pressure by 6 psi, the pump is *dropping* the pressure a full 5 psi! That sudden drop in pressure is going to take the air that *had* been absorbed in the water and release it.

You thought you got the air out of the water when you purged the system, didn't you? I'll bet you didn't count on this. Now you're going to have to go upstairs and start bleeding the radiators if you want to get paid.

And remember, the radiator with the *worst* air problem will **always** be the one behind the 200-gallon fish tank. Have a nice day.

Pump Location Didn't Use To Matter That Much

Twenty years ago, when all we had were 1750-rpm, low-head pumps, it really didn't matter where you put the pump on a residential job. But since the industry has embraced these small, high-speed pumps **that are capable of producing twice as much head pressure**, pump location suddenly makes a significant difference.

You don't have to be concerned that these little pumps will drop your system pressure into a sub-atmospheric condition on residential work. That's not the problem. You're filling residential systems to a minimum of 12 psi, and those little pumps aren't powerful enough to exceed that pressure.

But they *can* make your life more difficult when they're pumping toward the compression tank because they *will* drop the system pressure by nearly half when they start. Their location makes it much more difficult to rid the system of air.

If you get into the habit of moving the circulator to the supply side, "pumping away" from the compression tank, you're going to find that the radiators purge themselves in most cases. I know people who haven't bled a radiator in years, all because of their habit of "pumping away." And this includes diverter tee systems as well!

The pump can work for you or against you, it's your choice. Most boiler manufacturers will continue to supply packaged boilers with the pump on the return side because they have nothing to gain by moving it to the supply side. They'd have to build stronger crates, change their literature and their production line. And after all that trouble, they probably wouldn't sell one additional boiler.

It's really *your* choice, and you know what? That's the way it *should* be because you're the one who benefits on the job.

Unless you really enjoy bleeding radiators that is.

Pumps And Feed Valves

Now, this is *really* important: There's only one correct place to connect your feed valve: the point of no pressure change. This is the only place in the system where the pump can't affect the pressure. Pipe your feed valve there, and you'll never have a problem. Pipe it elsewhere, and as the pump changes the system pressure, the feed valve might get confused and make a serious mistake.

Here, let me lay out a situation for you. Let's say you install a residential system and fill it to 12 psi. You'll use the circulator that came with the boiler, a small, high-speed pump that can create about 6 psi of differential pressure. You leave the circulator where it is, but remember, since it's on the return side, discharging toward the compression tank, it can't raise the system's pressure above 12 psi at the compression tank.

If you were to put gauges on either side of the circulator, you'd see a discharge pressure of 13 psi and a suction pressure of 7 psi (representing the 6 psi differential across the pump). The discharge pressure goes up by 1 psi to reflect the pressure drop across the boiler and the near-boiler piping. The balance of the pressure differential shows up as a drop in suction pressure.

On this job, you decided to pipe the feed valve into the pump suction because that seemed to be as good a place as any. When you took the feed valve out of the box, you noticed the manufacturer had set it to feed whenever the system pressure dropped below 12 psi. That's okay with you; 12 psi is fine for a two-story house.

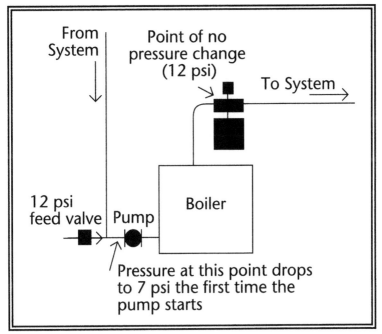

From System

Point of no pressure change (12 psi)

To System

12 psi feed valve | Pump

Boiler

Pressure at this point drops to 7 psi the first time the pump starts

Now, here's the problem. *On the very first cycle*, the pressure at the point where the feed valve connects to the system drops to 7 psi! Naturally, the feed valve feeds, bringing the system pressure back up to 12 psi. This happens while the circulator is running.

But wait a minute. That 7 psi reading the feed valve sensed when the pump started for the first time was an artificial reading, wasn't it? But how was the feed valve to know that? It fed because it sensed a drop in pressure. That's its job.

Now watch carefully. When the circulator stops, the gauge at the pump suction will read 17 psi instead of 12 psi. It's 5 psi higher than it was before because the feed valve added water to the compression tank while the circulator was running. Since the air in the tank is more compressed now than it was before (because of the extra water), the static fill pressure of the system is higher than it was before. In this case, it's 17 psi.

Think about that for a minute.

Now, this only happens once. The next time the circulator starts, it will drop its suction pressure by 5 psi again, and it will raise its discharge pressure by 1 psi. But the feed valve won't feed the second time *because the 5 psi drop at the pump's suction only lowers the system pressure to 12 psi*, the feed valve's setting.

This may not seem like a problem to you. After all, the relief valve won't pop until the pressure reaches 30 psi, and with the system at 17 psi, you still have plenty of leeway.

But there's something else to consider here. If you're going to raise the system fill pressure, you also have to pump up the air side of the diaphragm expansion tank. For things to work as they should, the two **must** match.

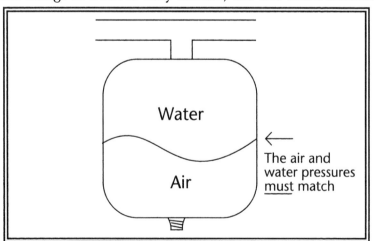

Water

Air

← The air and water pressures <u>must</u> match

Think about it. Since most residential systems need a 12-psi, water-fill pressure, most tank manufacturers precharge their tanks with 12 psi air pressure. But if you put one of these precharged tanks in a three-story house, you have to pump up the air side of the tank to 18 psi before you install it, don't you? If you don't, the tank will be about half the size of what you need at the higher pressure.

Did you know that?

One of the things on which a tank manufacturer bases a tank's size is the difference between the fill pressures and the relief pressure. If you increase the fill pressure by 50%, say, from 12 psi to 18 psi, you need twice as much tank.

In the example I just laid out for you, the feed valve brought the system pressure up to 17 psi on the first pumping cycle. That's nearly a 50% increase in fill pressure. Since you didn't pump up air in the tank (Who knew this was going to happen?), **the tank is now half the size of what the system needs for proper expansion.**

I'll bet your relief valve mysteriously pops when the system comes up to temperature. I'll also bet your tank fails long before its time because with only 12 psi on the air side, the expanding water is going to put an *awful* lot of stress on that diaphragm.

This is why the *only* proper location for a feed valve is at the point of no pressure change. That's the one place in the system the pump can't touch. It's the one place where the feed valve won't get confused. You'll **never** go wrong if you pipe it there.

"So How About Leaving The Pump Where It Is, And Just Move The Tank?"

In their installation booklet, a well-known boiler manufacturer shows what seems to be a really good idea. They leave the pump where it is (on the return side of their packaged boiler), and move the compression tank to the suction side of the pump.

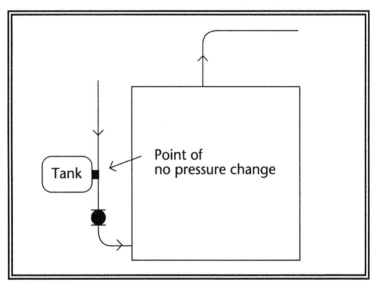

The pump is now "pumping away" from the compression tank and increasing the system's pressure. It's driving system air into solution and helping the contractor avoid problems. The manufacturer probably figures this is great because they don't have to move the pump from where they're used to putting it, and neither do you. It looks like you're getting the best of both worlds.

But there are a couple of potential problems with this piping arrangement. First, suppose you have a 30 psi boiler serving a tall building where the system fill pressure has to be about 25 psi in order to lift water to the top and pressurize it. When the pump comes on, it's going to add its pressure to the 25 psi fill pressure that's already inside the boiler and pop the relief valve.

That's what happens when the pump's pressure suddenly appears inside the boiler.

When you pipe your compression tank and pump on the **supply side**, "pumping away" from the boiler, the pump's pressure can't appear inside the boiler. The pump's pressure hits the system piping, not the boiler. As the water flows back to the boiler, friction from the system will reduce the pump's pressure to a point where it can't pop the relief valve.

But there's another, potentially more-serious, problem with this tank-on-the-return piping arrangement. Here, suppose you add a second pumped zone to the system.

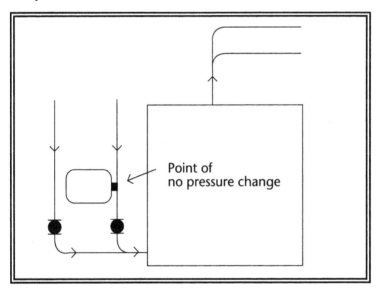

Point of
no pressure change

As things are now, one pump has the compression tank on its suction, the other pump has the tank on its discharge. One is pumping away from the point of no pressure change, the other isn't. The other is pumping **toward** it. One pump will increase its discharge pressure, the other will lower its suction pressure.

And look where that leads you.

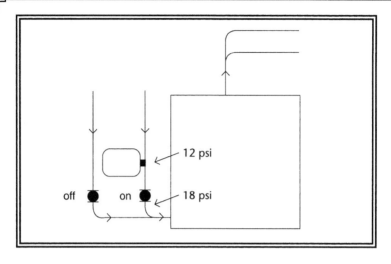

The pump on the discharge side of the compression tank works fine by itself. It adds its full pressure differential of 6 psi to the system fill pressure and creates 18 psi pressure at its discharge. The boiler has a 30 psi relief valve so you don't have to worry about the pump popping the relief valve. This pump works well.

Now let's see what happens when the other pump starts.

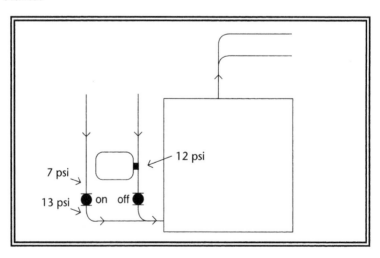

This pump is pumping **toward** the point of no pressure change (the compression tank). It manages to raise its discharge pressure, but only by 1 psi. The balance of its pressure differential shows up as a drop in suction pressure. But that's okay because only this zone is calling. The pump is running by itself. As long as its discharge pressure is higher than its suction pressure, water will flow.

But suppose both zones call at the same time. What happens then?

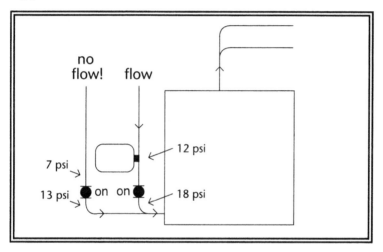

The "pumping away" pump develops its full 18 psi discharge pressure and back-pressures the other pump! Both pumps run, but water flows only through the zone that has the "pumping away" pump.

Can you see the problem? You can't enter a pipe charged to 18 psi with a pump only capable of producing 13 psi. That would be like trying to put 30 pounds of air in your tires with an air compressor set at 20 psi. It's impossible.

The trouble is, from the outside, the problem will look *exactly* like an air problem. The pump is running, but the radiation is cold. You'll bleed the zone, but get little or no air when you do. Then, when you run the "no heat" zone by itself, it will work well. You'll think you solved the problem. But on the next frigid day when both zones call at the same time, the problem will come back to haunt you. (This is a good time to remember one of the Golden Rules of Hydronic Heating: *If you bleed a radiator and you don't get air, it **ain't** an air problem. Stop bleeding!*)

To solve this particular problem, you can either move the compression tank to the supply side of the boiler, or you can put the tank and both pumps on the supply side, "pumping away" from the point of no pressure change.

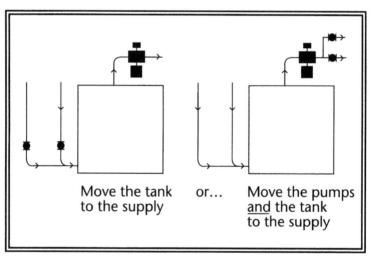

Move the tank   or...   Move the pumps
to the supply   <u>and</u> the tank
                                      to the supply

If you move only the compression tank, you won't be able to use the pumps' differential pressure to help you rid the system of air-related problems. In other words, you'll be right back where you started. On the other hand, if you move the tank **and** the pumps to the supply side of the boiler, you'll have a quieter and less-troublesome system. You'll be a happier, and yes, a better-looking, person.

It's up to you, bub.

You Won't Be The First!

Only about 6% of the buildings in the United States have hydronic heating systems (and that includes hot water **and** steam heat). In Europe and Asia, by contrast, nearly 100% of the buildings are hydronically heated, and literally all of it is hot water.

If you travel to those foreign countries, you'll be hard pressed to find a heating system where the pumps are installed on the return side of the boiler. Those folks know about the point of no pressure change and they respect it.

I remember having a conversation with a heating installer in Germany a few years ago. I mentioned that in the U.S., most contractors install the pumps on the return side of the boilers, pumping toward the compression tanks.

"You must have a lot of air problems!" he exclaimed.

"We have air problems up the wazoo," I admitted. "Some guys make a living out of bleeding radiators where I come from. Entire industries have sprung up around the problem."

"Why don't you move the pumps?" he asked.

"Because most of us are slaves to habit," I explained.

"Why do your boiler manufacturers put the pumps on the return in the first place?" he wondered, scratching his head.

"Packaging convenience," I explained.

His eyes grew wide. "You let the *packaging people* do your engineering?"

"I never thought of it that way, but, yeah, I suppose we do," I admitted.

"Then why don't your contractors just move the pumps? They're the ones who get stuck with the problems on the jobs, aren't they? The noises, the bleeding of the radiators, the expensive callbacks. Why don't the

contractors do something about it?"

"Oh, the smart ones do." I told him. "The smart ones do."

"Pumping Away" Piping

Since you've read this far, I figure you must be pretty open-minded. You may even be willing to break a few old habits - if it's to your advantage, I mean. I wouldn't want you to do it for any other reason. There's **gotta** be something in it for you.

And that's why I'd like you to give this piping arrangement some consideration. There's *a lot* in it for you.

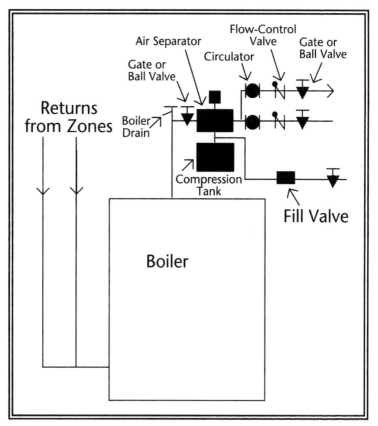

You leave the boiler with a full-size supply main and enter a tee. Pipe a ¹/₂" boiler drain into the top of the tee. That's going to be the purge valve for your system. You only need one purge valve. You take the money you were going to spend on the other purge valves and you go buy something nice for yourself.

Now, come off the side of the tee, keeping the pipe full size as you go, and install either a ball valve or a gate valve. You'll be using this valve for service, as well as for your initial air purge.

Your air separator comes next. If you're using a scoop- or orifice-type air separator, you'll need to allow 18 inches of straight, full-size horizontal pipe at the inlet to the air separator. The manufacturers of these types of air separators call for this approach piping. They need it to get the maximum efficiency out of their units. If you're using a microbubble reabsorber-type of air separator, you won't need this approach piping; you can install this type of air separator right next to the ball or gate valve.

Okay, next we have the compression tank. You'll attach it to, or very near, the air separator. In this example, I'm using a diaphragm-type tank. I'll show you how to use a plain-steel tank in a minute.

Bring your feed valve into the line connecting the diaphragm tank to the system piping. That's the point of no pressure change, the only place in the system where the pump can't affect the feed valve. You'll be using the feed valve, the main service valve and the tee-mounted boiler drain to power purge the air from the system. You push it all in one direction.

That's one of the best things about this piping arrangement. It lets you power purge *toward* the system piping and up through the bottom of the boiler. You can power purge one zone at a time and never wind up with a big bubble of air trapped inside the boiler. This, whether you realize it or not, often happens when you pipe your feed valve into the boiler and your purge valves on the return. You need that one main shut-off valve to get everything going in the same direction.

Okay, next come your circulators. Here, I'm using two, but you can have as many as you'd like. After each circulator, you'll pipe in a flow-control valve to prevent gravity circulation and short-circuiting, and then a ball or gate valve for service and the initial power purge.

If you prefer to zone with valves instead of circulators, pipe the job like this.

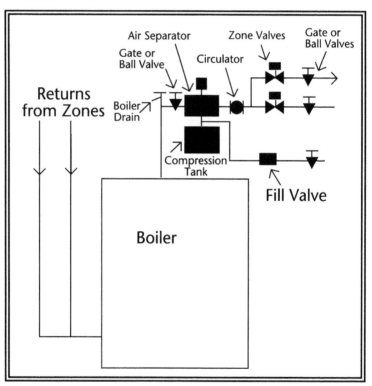

In either case, you'll get rid of your initial air by closing the main service valve and the zone service valves. Next, open the feed valve and the tee-mounted boiler drain. Then, open one zone at a time. It's like firing torpedoes.

The water will flow through the first zone, pushing air ahead of itself. The air will zip through the boiler and leave the system by way of the tee-mounted boiler drain. The water will also fill the boiler.

When the water runs air-free, close that zone's service valve and open the next zone's service valve. Bam! The water will push the air through the second zone and the already-filled boiler.

If you have a dozen zones, do this a dozen times. You only need that one power purge valve, and you won't wind up with that big bubble in the boiler.

When you start the system, the pumps will add their differential pressure to the system's static fill pressure and move whatever air comes out of the heated water back to the air separator.

In most cases, you'll find you don't have to go upstairs to bleed the radiators. You'll be doing it all from the basement - even on diverter-tee systems! The system will run quietly, with no pinging or waterfall sounds. You've put the combined forces of Boyle's Law and Henry's Law and Mother Nature on your side.

You may never have to bleed a radiator again.

One guy took me up on this challenge a few years ago. He tried it on a diverter-tee system and then he called me at home.

"Dan," he said, "I have **never** run across a diverter-tee system that didn't make me crazy. It usually takes me over an hour to get rid of the air, and that's what I thought would happen here, but I was willing to give it a shot because I figured you had nothing to gain by lying to me."

"That's right," I admitted. "Whether you put the pump on the supply or the return, it doesn't put a nickel in *my* pocket. I only tell you these things because they're true."

"Well," he continued, "I started the pump and went

out to my truck to get a can and a rag and a screwdriver. Not that I seriously doubted you or anything. I just figured you *might be* full of bull so I might as well get ready."

"And what happened," I asked.

"Well, when I got to the first convector, it was already hot!"

"How about that!" I said.

"And every other one was hot as well," he explained. "I've never seen anything like this!"

"That's what happens when you work with your **head** as well as your hands," I told him. "You have Mother Nature and Mr. Boyle and Mr. Henry on your side now."

"You know, you're not as dumb as you look," he said.

"I couldn't possibly be," I admitted.

Steel Compression Tanks

In some cases, you may want to use a steel compression tank instead of a diaphragm-type tank. I say that because on most retrofit jobs, the steel compression tanks is free! It's already hanging there from the ceiling. It's not leaking. It has no moving parts. And the home owner thinks his domestic hot water comes from there.

So why argue with the guy?

Oh, but I know why you want to get rid of that steel tank. It constantly waterlogs. It creates callbacks and angry customers. You've had bad experiences over the years. I know all the reasons.

It doesn't have to be that way, though. Not if you understand what's going on. Not if you set the system up right. Here, look.

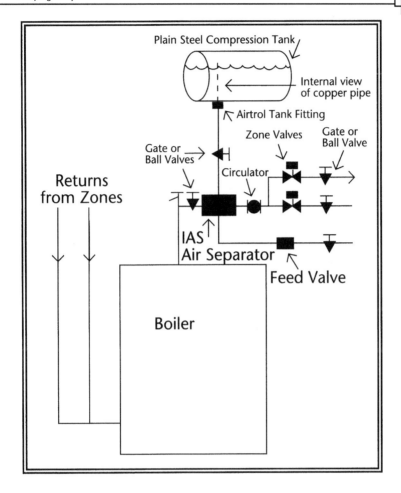

Plain Steel Compression Tank

Internal view of copper pipe

Airtrol Tank Fitting

Zone Valves

Gate or Ball Valve

Gate or Ball Valves

Circulator

Returns from Zones

IAS
Air Separator

Feed Valve

Boiler

I like to use Bell & Gossett's IAS orifice-type air separator with a steel tank because I can take advantage of the 3/4" tapping they provide. They oversize that tapping so you can use it for either an air vent or a tank line.

The line leading from the system to the compression tank should *never* be smaller than 3/4" because the air captured by the separator will be moving up this line to its new home inside the compression tank. The tank line has to slope continuously upward so the separated air can rise into the tank by its buoyancy.

I also like to use Bell & Gossett's Airtrol Tank Fitting at the inlet to a steel compression tank. This device has been around for many years, but most installers don't fully understand what it does. Its job is to prevent gravity circulation between the hot water in the distribution piping and the cooler water in the tank.

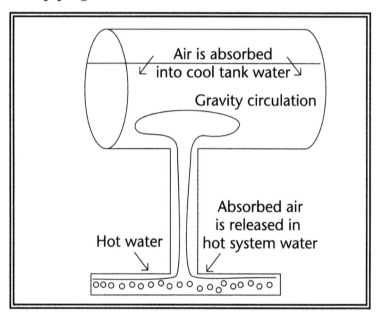

The water in the tank is cooler than the water in the system because the pump isn't moving any water in and out of the tank. Since the tank water is relatively cool, it absorbs some of the tank's air cushion.

The cooler tank water then falls by gravity down the 3/4" line as hotter system water migrates up from the piping to take its place. Don't confuse this gravity exchange of hot and cold water with a pumped flow in and out of the tank. It's very different.

When the cooler, air-laden water from the tank reaches the hot system, the air that had been absorbed into solution up in the tank comes *out* of solution in the system piping or the boiler (depending on where you've attached the tank line). The next time the pump starts, it moves those tiny air bubbles out to the radiators where they're vented to the atmosphere when you bleed the radiators.

When the air bubbles leave the system by way of the automatic or manual vents, the system pressure drops slightly and the feed valve opens to add water. The fresh water enters the compression tank (the only place that can accommodate it) and raises its level. Over the course of a heating season, you wind up with a water-logged tank.

But if you could **prevent** gravity circulation between the tank and the system, you could keep the tank from waterlogging. This is where the Airtrol Tank Fitting comes in. Its job is to keep the cooler, air-laden water from migrating down into the system. It does this with a simple baffle, and a copper tube. It has no moving parts. When you set up the Airtrol Tank Fitting properly, it does a fine job of keeping the air where it belongs - in the tank.

You'll notice in the system drawing that there's a gate or full-port ball valve in the 3/4" line going up to the tank. With this piping arrangement, you'll be filling the tank last, and that's why you need the valve.

Start by shutting the valve in the tank line, and opening the little drain tapping in the bottom of the Airtrol Tank Fitting. Then, power purge the system as I described before - toward the zones, one at a time, and back through the boiler. When you get all the air out, close the tee-mounted boiler drain and open the tank's valve. The water will rush up into the tank, and the air will leave through the Airtrol Tank Fitting's drain tapping.

That drain, by the way, is attached to a thin copper line that extends two-thirds of the way up into the tank. That's the correct air-to-water ratio for a steel compression tank. If the tank is properly sized, you should always have ²/₃ water and ¹/₃ air on start-up. You'll know the level is correct when water begins to squirt from the Airtrol Tank Fitting's drain. Shut the drain, and remove the handle from the valve in the tank line so the home owner won't accidentally shut it (if he did, the relief valve would pop).

As soon as you start the pumps, they'll pressurize the system water and move any residual air back to the air separator. The air separator will capture it and direct it up into the steel compression tank where it will remain for years to come.

If have this set-up in my own house. The compression tank was installed in 1950. It has an Airtrol Tank Fitting. I have no air noises whatsoever, and I've never had a waterlogged tank. It's hard to argue with success.

Built-In Air Separators

Nowadays, some cast-iron boiler manufacturers build air separators right into their boilers. It's part of the casting process. They create a baffle near the boiler's supply tapping and use the boiler as a low-velocity chamber to separate air from the water as both pass through the boiler. The air, which moves relatively slowly because the boiler creates a "wide space in the road," rises by its buoyancy and gets trapped by the baffle. The heated water continues out to the system.

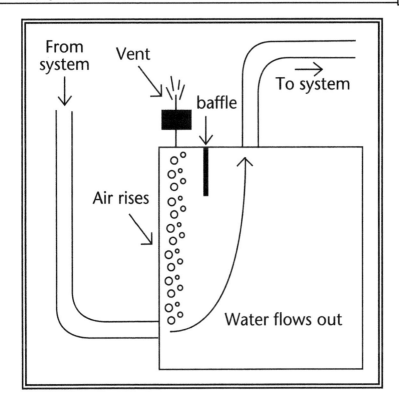

This isn't a new idea; boiler manufacturers used it on their boilers during the 1940s. It is, however, a relatively effective device if you're zoning with valves and using just one pump. I've found, though, that if you're zoning with pumps instead of valves, the combined flow rate when all the pumps call is often so great that the air slips under the baffle and winds up in the radiators anyway. This isn't a new lesson; old-timers learned it during the 1940s. Built-in air separators work best with a single pump.

If you decide to use it, set your system up like this.

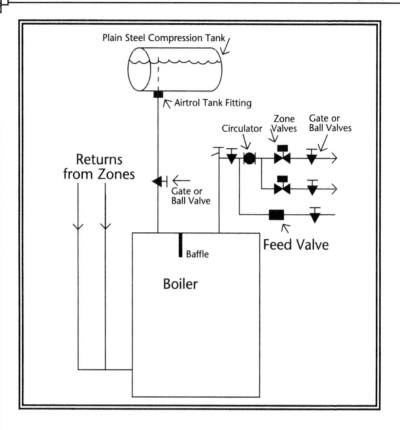

Here, you're using the steel tank you found hanging from the basement ceiling. You've attached a ³/₄" copper line from the boiler's built-in air separator to a B&G Airtrol Tank Fitting mounted in the steel tank. You put a **gate or full-port** ball valve in the tank's line so it won't interfere with the rising air bubbles.

You've kept the supply line full size up through your power purge tee. You have a main service valve (also full size) and then a tee with a ¹/₂" branch connection for your feed valve. After that comes the pump, the zone valves and their individual service valves.

You start this system in the same way you did the others. Just make sure you fill the tank last.

The reason you have the feed line where it is instead

of at the point of no pressure change is so you can power purge toward the system and through the bottom of the boiler. In this case, it's to your advantage to have the feed line on the other size of the main service valve. Just make sure you keep the supply line full size to the feed tee. That will minimize the pump's suction-side pressure drop and give you the maximum benefit.

I know I'm getting away from the textbook here, but as long as you keep the pipe full size and as short as possible up to the pump suction, it works well and it saves money. In fact, this is the lowest cost way I can think of to get the job done, and still take advantage of the benefits "pumping away" has to offer.

Here's the same set-up with a diaphragm-type tank.

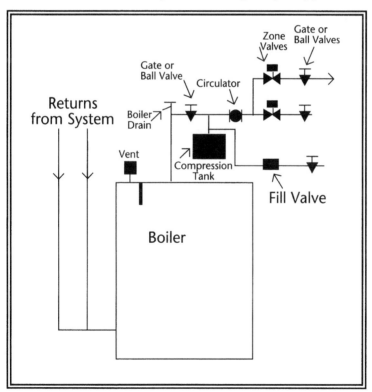

You're bringing the feed valve in at the tank, and you've put a good-quality automatic air vent in the boiler's air-separation tapping. Use a vent with a large capacity. Even though this is a residential boiler, you should take a look at commercial water vents. They last a long time, vent air quickly, close tightly and are well worth the few extra bucks they cost.

Start the system up the same way you did the others.

Good Habits

When you pipe your boilers in any of the ways I've mentioned, you're giving yourself easy access to all the mechanical components that are likely to need service. The circulators, zone valves, flow-control valves, the diaphragm tank, air vent and fill valve are all accessible to you now. All you have to do is close the one main gate or ball valve and the smaller gate or ball valves downstream of the flow-control valves or zone valves.

You also get to work standing up for a change. That would be nice, wouldn't it?

When you present it properly, "Pumping Away" can have tremendous appeal to home owners. Tell them you won't have to drain the entire system to get at any of the components that will most likely need service as the years go by. Tell them you'll be able to get the service call done quickly. Mention that, should the system need service during the day, they won't have to miss much time from work. Tell them you won't have to traipse around upstairs, moving furniture and bleeding radiators (and keep in mind, upstairs is where most of *your* liability problems begin!). Tell them their system will run quieter and more efficiently because it won't be air-bound. Air-bound radiators often make the burner run longer.

"Pumping Away" makes *your* story different from

the other guy's story. It sets you apart from the pack. It addresses the ***building owner's*** self-interests. And believe it or not, it usually costs ***less*** to install this way!

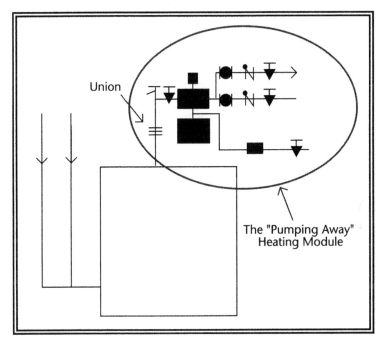

Union

The "Pumping Away"
Heating Module

If you add a union to the vertical supply pipe, you can build a "Pumping Away Heating Module" in your shop and just connect it to the boiler when you get to the job. A friend told me he cut his installation time in half by using this technique. He commented, "If they can build modular homes, why can't I build modular heating systems?" Good question, eh? He just carries the packaged boiler concept a few steps further.

He told me he just shows up on the day of installation with the boiler and the manifold. He connects the union and the rest of the job is just soldering. He says he's doing twice as many boilers a day since he "got organized."

Something to think about, isn't it?

If you build the module in your shop, you can test it with water or air pressure to make sure it doesn't leak. Let's face it, most of your leaks on a boiler replacement will be in the iron pipe. This way, you'll fix any leaks in your shop. Your customer never has to see them.

You won't have to bring your pipe-cutting tools to the job. That saves time and money. You'll also make less of a mess in your customer's house and take up less space outside. You won't spill cutting oil on the ground, and you'll work more quietly than any of your competitors. Tell the people these things. They're all great selling points.

You can have one of your young mechanics put the manifold together in your shop where you have all the right tools, and a vice, and a workbench, and good lighting. It's a great place for a young person to learn - and you can watch and guide them while you're preparing to make money.

I could go on and on. My main point in all of this is that I want you to **win** by using your head as well as your hands on that next job. The world is *full* of opportunity for someone willing to question old habits - and then break them, if they suddenly don't make too much sense anymore.

"Pumping Away" makes *lots* of sense.

But Then Again...
(An Actual Conversation)

Contractor: *"I can't possibly move that pump from the return to the supply."*

Me: *"Why not?"*

Contractor: *"The piece of BX is too short!"*

Me: *"They sell BX in long rolls. They really do."*

Contractor: *"That ain't the point!"*

Some *Really* Cool Piping Options

"Do this now: Think about what a British Thermal Unit looks like, how big it is, what is feels like, how much it weighs, what color it is. And when you've got it all figured out, go describe it to some little kid. Don't stop describing until you make her see that Btu in her mind's eye. Make that kid smile with delight.

"Then go talk to the people. They'll hear the pictures in your head, and they'll buy what you're selling: **Comfort!**"

One-Pipe, Baseboard Loop Systems

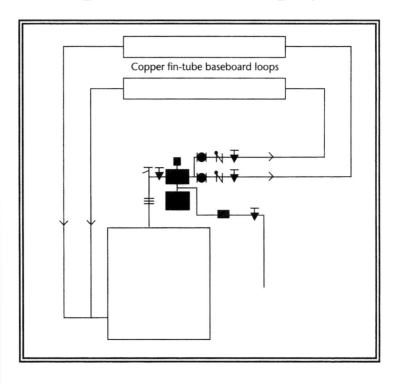

Copper fin-tube baseboard loops

The simplest type of hydronic heating you can install is the baseboard loop system. The piping runs to and from the boiler and through each room in a continuous loop. Since the water gives up its heat as it flows through the radiation, it will be cooler at the end of the loop than it is at the beginning. You'll have to compensate for the lessened output at the end of the run by using more fin tube in those rooms.

Most installers don't worry about this, though. They find it easier just to run fin tube from wall to wall in every room. If there's an outside wall, they cover it with fin tube. They figure this gives them full perimeter heat and protects them, no matter how cold it gets outside.

But it really doesn't make sense to use more baseboard than the room's heat loss calls for. You're wasting money (yours!) if you do, and you're creating hot and cold spots in the building as well. If you take the time to do a heat loss calcuation, you'll save money on every job. You might even ***get*** more jobs because your price will be more competitive. *[Nowadays, there are many software programs available to do heat-loss calculations. Slant/Fin's Hydronic Explorer 2 is one of these programs, and you can get a free copy by visiting the Slant/Fin website at www.slantfin.com. Just scroll to Heat Loss Software on their navigation bar. You can ask for a disc or download the program directly from their site.]*

By "pumping away," even on such a simple system, you'll avoid the pinging and waterfall noises that often plague these systems, and you'll be setting yourself apart from your competitors. Follow-up service will be a snap, and it will probably take less time to install and start-up than you're used to spending now.

One-Pipe, Diverter-Tee Systems

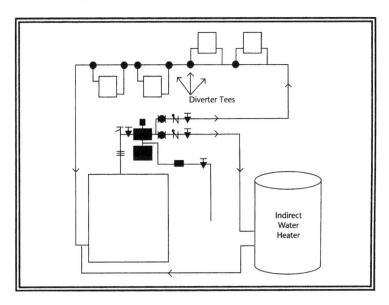

Diverter-tee systems split the flow and send some of the supply water to the radiation while the rest continues along the main. How much water flows to each radiator depends on the pressure drop between the tees that connect the radiator to the main.

There are a few rules you have to follow when you work with these systems:

❏ If the radiator is above the main, you'll probably only need one diverter tee. It goes on the return side. Depending on the manufacturer, the tees can be as close as six inches apart for a radiator above the main, however, the manufacturers had convectors in mind when they wrote this guideline. Don't expect to be able to feed hot water through a long run of baseboard if the tees are that close together. The pressure drop to and from the radiator will probably be too great, and most of the water will bypass the branch and flow through the main instead. It makes for a head-scratching, no-heat call. It looks just like an air problem, but when you bleed the baseboard, you won't get any air. Try to think like water. What would you do?

❏ If the radiator is below the main, you **have to** use two diverter tees and they **must** be as wide apart as the radiator. This is really important because the water is hot and buoyant and it doesn't want to go down. You have to help it by inducing a hefty pressure drop along the main. The two diverter tees, and the proper spacing between them, usually create the right pressure drop and direct the water down through the radiator.

Diverter-tee systems are especially difficult to purge because the flow of water splits so many times. The air always seems to find a place to hide. This is where "pumping away" really shines because instead of dropping the system pressure and pulling air **out** of solution, the pumps pressurize the high-point air and drive it **into** the water. In most cases, you'll find you never have to leave the basement to get all the radiators hot. The one exception will be when you have bottom-connected, cast-iron radiators. Because of their large internal spaces and low flow velocities, you'll most likely have to vent these manually. But these radiators are usually easy to get to.

As the water flows through each radiator and blends back into the supply line, it will lower the temperature that's available to the next radiator. The temperature drop from radiator to radiator won't be as dramatic here as it is in a loop system, though, because only a portion of the water flows through each radiator. The rest passes along the main without losing many Btus.

Two-Pipe, Direct-Return Systems

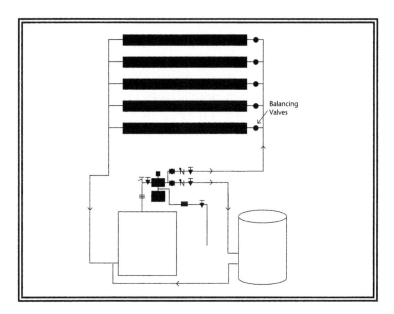

Balancing
Valves

Used mostly in larger buildings, the two-pipe, direct-return system offers the system designer a real advantage. Because it's set up like a ladder (with the supply and return mains being the sides, and the radiators, the rungs), this system provides each radiator with basically the same supply water temperature. The only drop in temperature from radiator to radiator comes from the heat loss through the supply piping. If you insulate the mains, you'll hardly notice that drop in temperature.

Flow balancing is the real challenge with these systems. Water is lazy. It always wants to short-circuit across the radiators that are closest to the boiler; it doesn't want to flow out to the ends of the run.

You can solve this problem by flow balancing the system. This involves throttling the flow across the near-boiler radiators, making it tougher for the water to take its short-cut. If the water can't go that way, it will move out along the main and flow through the far radiators.

Keep in mind the water will *always* follow the path of least resistance. By balancing the flow through each radiator, you'll be eliminating that path. You'll make the pressure drop through each "rung of the ladder" the same. The water will have no choice other than to flow everywhere.

On many large, commercial jobs, mechanical engineers will specify a special type of balancing fitting they can pre-set on paper. When the installer follows the engineer's "degree of opening" instructions, the system will more or less go into balance on start-up. Then, the installer will use a differential-pressure meter, which the balancing-fitting manufacturer provides, to fine-tune the flow through the system.

By "pumping away" on these larger jobs, you'll avoid the air-related problems that sometimes occur in areas where the flow velocity is low. You'll also eliminate the possibility that the pump might drop its suction pressure and bring air into the system. The system will start up easily and run quietly, and you won't be nervous when the phone rings.

Thermostatic Radiator Valves

Two-pipe systems are very well suited to thermostatic radiator valves.

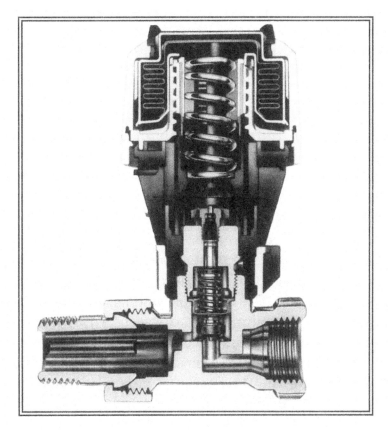

These units come in two parts and are self-contained. The valve is spring-loaded and normally open. You pipe it at the inlet to the radiator. The valve operator snaps onto the valve body. It contains a temperature-sensitive chemical that expands and contracts against the valve's stem in response to changes in the room's air temperature. As the air in the room gets warmer, the operator throttles the flow of hot water through the radiator and limits the radiator's heat output. As the room cools, the operator contracts and lets more hot water enter the radiator.

Thermostatic radiator valves quickly compensate for heat gain or loss in individual rooms. They do a good job of temperature-balancing systems since they throttle or shut down completely when the room reaches whatever temperature you've selected (typically, from 50 - 90 degrees Fahrenheit)

When you use thermostatic radiator valves, your circulator will run continuously during the heating season. You can turn it on with a manual switch, or you can use a simple control to have it come on when the outdoor temperature drops below a preset point.

Because there will be times during the fall and spring when a mild outdoor temperature will keep many or all of the thermostatic radiator valves closed, you have to give some thought to where the water will go on those days if it can't flow through the radiators. Remember, the pump has no way of knowing the valves are closed. There's no wiring between the two.

If you run the pump against closed valves you'll be "dead-heading" it. The energy of motion will quickly turn to heat and build up pressure inside the pump body. Dead-headed pumps can suddenly explode with great violence and make your sphincter muscle do the mambo. Ask me how I know that.

The best way to avoid this problem is to install a differential-pressure bypass line between the supply and return line on the **radiation side** of the pump.

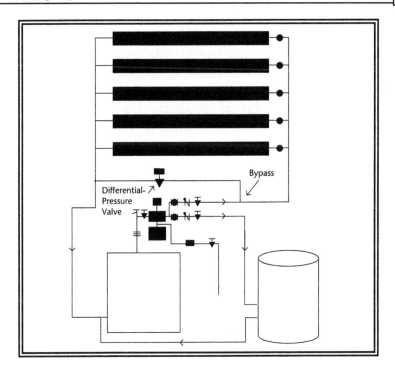

You'll set this inexpensive, spring-loaded valve to be completely closed when all the thermostatic radiator valves are wide open. As the valves begin to close, the bypass will sense the rise in pump pressure and open slightly to channel the unused supply water back to the return side of the boiler.

Unfortunately, even though differential-pressure valves aren't expensive, some installers don't like to spend a nickel more than they think they have to. Instead of using the valve, they'll just pipe a small line from supply to return, figuring the water will bypass that way when the thermostatic radiator valves begin to close. The trouble with this is that the bypass line can't tell how much water needs to be bypassed. This often leads to velocity noise that can transmit throughout the system.

A differential-pressure valve is the **real** solution. It

can sense the exact amount of water the system needs at any time. It also has the ability to create a supply-to-return pressure drop, eating up the pump's head pressure before sending the water back into the boiler. By doing this, the valve prevents the pump from applying its full discharge pressure inside the boiler when it's in the full-bypass mode. If you use a wide-open bypass line, the pump might pop the relief valve when it starts.

What you save on the valve, you'll spend on callbacks - many times over.

When you use thermostatic radiator valves, every radiator becomes an independent zone. They're a terrific solution to over-heated areas, and many building owners would consider them - if only they knew about them. So tell them.

(Thermostatic radiator valves on one-pipe systems)

You can also use thermostatic radiator valves on loop or diverter-tee systems. You just have to know the limitations.

In a loop system, all the water passes through all the radiators, so if you want to use thermostatic radiator valves, you have to give the water a place to go when the first valve closes. If you don't, all flow will stop.

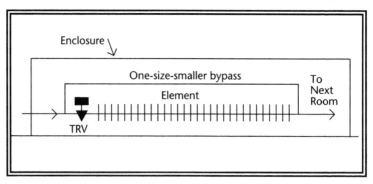

Install your thermostatic radiator valves in the loop piping, just as it enters each room. Size the valve to match the pipe size of the baseboard, then use a pipe one size smaller than the baseboard to run a bypass over the top of the element. For instance, you'll use $1/2$" to bypass around $3/4$" , and $3/4$" to bypass around 1". The baseboard enclosure conceals the bypass; the thermostatic radiator valve's controller sticks out through the cover.

As the room comes up to temperature, the thermostatic radiator valve will throttle the flow through the element, and send a portion of the hot water through the bypass and on to the next room. Naturally, you'll get less water through the bypass than you will through the element, but since the thermostatic radiator valves are closing, you won't need as much water down the line anyway. It all works out.

Thermostatic radiator valves improve the performance of a loop system by preventing overheating and giving the customer the ability to maintain different temperatures within the same loop zone. It's another one of those things home owners don't know about.

So tell them, for Pete's sake.

As to thermostatic radiator valves and diverter-tee systems, you may get mixed results here. How well they work depends a lot on the pressure drop between the two tees.

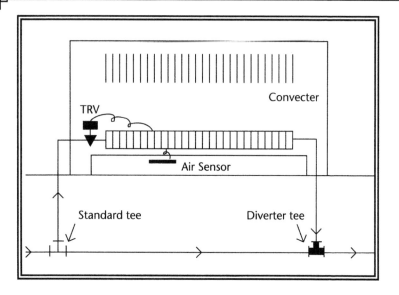

The water will **always** favor the path of least resistance. This is the principle that makes the diverter tee system work. The original installer figured out how much water he wanted to divert through the radiator. He selected the tee or tees that would give him the right flow rate **at a certain pressure drop across the radiator.**

By adding a thermostatic radiator valve to the branch circuit, however, you'll increase the pressure drop through the branch line and slow the flow of hot water through the radiator. You may wind up with a "not enough heat" call on a very cold day.

The trick with these systems is to select a thermostatic radiator valve with a very low pressure drop. If the pressure drop is too high, the water may choose to go straight along the main instead of diverting through the branch that leads to the radiator. When that happens, you can wind up with no heat, even though the thermostatic radiator valve is wide open.

When you read through a thermostatic radiator valve manufacturer's literature, look for a rating called

Cv. It will read Cv = (some number). This number represents the flow rate in gallons per minute that must pass through the valve in order to produce a pressure drop of 1 psi. The higher the Cv number, the lower the valve's pressure drop. For diverter-tee systems, it's best to select a thermostatic radiator valve with the highest possible Cv.

If you're not sure what to use, talk with the manufacturer or their representative. Let them know you're planning to use the valves on a diverter-tee system, and ask for advice.

If they tell you not to worry about it, ***worry about it***, and then go talk to someone else.

Two-Pipe, Reverse-Return Systems

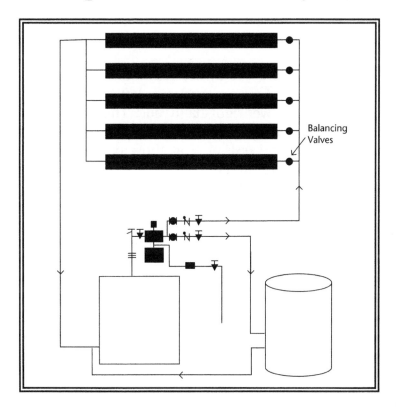

Balancing Valves

This system is similar to two-pipe, direct-return, with one major difference: it has a third pipe. That pipe makes sure that the traveling distance between the boiler and each radiator is exactly the same. The third pipe eliminates the path of least resistance as well as the need to use balancing valves at each radiator.

Here, compare reverse-return to direct return.

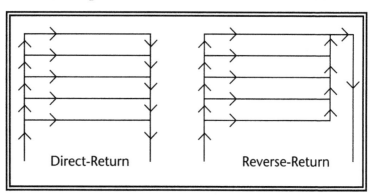

Direct-Return   Reverse-Return

A two-pipe, direct-return system looks like a ladder. You enter the system on the lower-left-hand side and leave from the lower-right-hand side. The water wants to short-circuit across the lower "rungs" of the ladder, so you have to add resistance at those points by throttling the balancing valves.

A two-pipe reverse-return system is similar, to a point. The water enters the system through the same pipe it used before, but now it leaves the grid through the **upper-right-hand** side. That's the opposite corner. It uses the third pipe to work its way back to the boiler.

Trace the water's path through any of the "rungs. Do you see how the traveling distance to and from each radiator is the same? That's why two-pipe, reverse-return systems go into balance as soon as you start the pump.

This, of course, assumes the radiation throughout the system is similar. Keep in mind that pressure drop is what's really important here. Pressure drop sets up the path water will favor and follow. If you set up a reverse-return system with, say, a convector, a length of copper fun-tube baseboard, a unit heater and an air-handling coil, chances are it won't work well because the pressure drop across each heating unit is wildly different. The traveling distance to and from them may be the same, but once the water reaches each heating unit, it has to work its way **through**. If it finds it easier to get through the baseboard than it does through the unit heater, for instance, it will always favor the baseboard - even though you have reverse-return piping.

The same reasoning applies if you're planning on zoning with thermostatic radiator valves. Here, too, it doesn't make much sense to go to the extra expense of installing a reverse-return piping system because the thermostatic radiator valves will throttle the flow and change the pressure drop from radiator to radiator anyway. With thermostatic radiator valves, you're better off with a direct-return system.

Reset - An Option That Makes Sense

Guess what. It doesn't get frigid every day of the year. You know that, and I know that. Unfortunately, we forgot to tell that to most of our hydronic heating systems. They operate as though every day were the coldest day of the year. Most work like mad to produce 180 degree (or hotter) water whether the outdoor air temperature reads 50 degrees or 10 degrees. This is the hydronic equivalent of driving your car with one foot on the gas and the other foot on the brake. Which is fine, I suppose, if you have a lot of money to spend on gasoline.

A reset control can bring sanity and savings to *any* hydronic system because it matches the heat input to the heat loss at any given moment. For instance, on a day when the outside temperature is 50 degrees, the reset control might send 100 degree water to the radiators. Should the outdoor temperature drop to 10 degrees later in the winter, the control will automatically raise the supply water temperature to 180 degrees to satisfy the heat loss on **that** day.

A reset control senses two things: supply (or sometimes, return) water temperature, and outdoor air temperature. It compares the two, and then shifts the supply water temperature along a curve (which you select when you set up the system) to find the right heat input for that moment.

A typical reset curve looks like this.

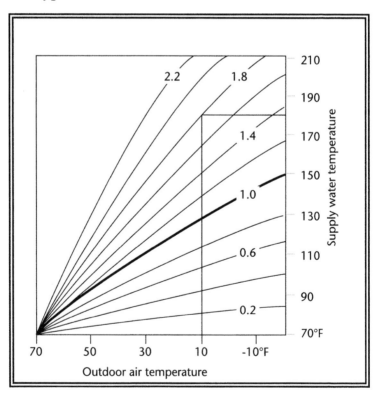

You turn a dial on the control to select one of the curves. Which one you need depends on how you design your system. For example, let's say you figure on having 180-degree water in the radiators on a day when the outside temperature is 10 degrees. You install enough radiation to get the job done with that temperature. Now, take a look at the point I marked on the curve. That's your reference point. The control will bring the water up to that temperature when it's 10 degrees outside.

But here's the best part. The reset control will automatically shift the water temperature ***down*** as the air temperature goes **up**. Take another look at the curve.

On a 30 degree day, the water temperature, in this case, will be about 145 degrees. Should the outdoor thermometer drift up to 50 degrees, the water temperature will slide down to 110 degrees. It's all automatic; you just set it up initially and from there, it takes over and does the rest.

Reset controls make sense in just about *any* hydronic system, but they're especially useful in radiant floor heating systems, as you'll see.

Radiant Floor-Heating Systems

Radiant floor heating is different from convective heating because it's more concerned with the heat loss from your *body* than it is with the heat loss from the room you're in. This is a key concept many people don't fully understand so I want to spend a few minutes explaining it to you.

First, you have to realize the human body is a "radiator" of sorts. It produces far more heat than it needs to survive, and it has to give up that excess heat to feel comfortable. It does this in three ways:

➡ **By evaporation (when we perspire and breath)**

➥ By convection (when air moves across our bodies)

➥ And, most important by radiation (because heat goes to cold).

Your body loses fully *half* of its heat by radiating it to surrounding objects. You *are* a radiator! When you stand next to something warmer than you, you feel hot. And when you stand near something cooler than you, you feel cold - regardless of the temperature of the surrounding air.

That's the important part. Air temperature is less important to comfort than you probably think. Here, consider this. You're standing behind a single-pane-glass storm door on a cold day, watching the world go by. The air in your house is warm, but you feel cold. How come? Well, there may be a draft coming through the door. That's a convection current, and it can, of course, cause your body to lose heat. But there's an even more significant reason why you feel chilly when you stand next to that single-pane glass door. Your body is a radiator. It's radiating heat toward the cold surface of the storm door. You lose *half* of your heat this way. Even though you're standing in 70-degree air, you're chilly.

Engineers call this phenomenon "Cold 70." It's what happens when there's too much of a difference between the air temperature and the temperature of the surrounding surfaces.

If you want to experience "Cold 70" in a very convincing way, go to your local supermarket and walk up and down the aisles. Make sure you take a thermometer with you (or pick one up in the housewares aisle).

Take note of the air temperature as you walk down the cereal aisle. Let's say it's 68 degrees. Notice how it's the same in canned foods, paper goods, juices and junk food.

Now, walk down the frozen-food aisle and check out the air temperature. It's the same! But you feel colder in the frozen-food aisle, don't you? Do you know why? It's because you're standing next to the cold surfaces of the freezer chests. The heat from your body is radiating toward the freezers. As you lose heat, you feel chilly, **even though the air is as warm as it is in every other aisle**.

Your body is a radiator.

"Cold 70" is what's wrong with most scorched air systems. A furnace can blow hot air down on you at high velocity, but since it's cycling on and off, the surfaces in the room often remain cold. And where there's a wide difference between the air temperature and the temperature of the room's surfaces, you're going to feel uncomfortable.

Radiant heat strives **to control the radiant heat loss from your body**. Its goal is to make the surfaces that surround you the same temperature as the surface of your clothed body. That temperature, by the way, is about 85 degrees, Fahrenheit.

If the surfaces that surround you are the same temperature as you, you'll feel comfortable, even though the air in the room might be five or more degrees cooler than you're used to having it with a convective system. In fact, many people say that at this lowered temperature, the air in the room feels fresher and more crisp, like outside air on a day in early fall.

Radiant floor heating doesn't produce convective air currents so it keeps the temperature of the air at the ceiling nearly the same as it is a foot or so above the floor. Because of this, there's less heat loss through the ceiling and there's less heat loss through infiltration.

It's true that radiant floor heating systems cost more to install, but they also operate at lower costs than any other type of heating system. And when properly designed, they provide unsurpassed comfort.

In a radiant floor heating system, the floor becomes the radiator, and because it's so large, it doesn't have to be that warm. It just has to be about 85 degrees, the same temperature as the outside of your clothed body. In fact, if the surface of the floor becomes hotter than 85 degrees, it becomes uncomfortable because it then forces your body to retain heat.

To make the floor 85 degrees, you have to circulate water that's hotter than 85 degrees through the buried tubing. If you embed radiant floor heat tubing in a concrete slab on grade or in lightweight-concrete poured over a subfloor, the typical high-limit temperature for the zone's water will be about 120 degrees, Fahrenheit. If you staple the tubing between the joists under a subfloor, the temperature will be higher, probably in the range of 150 - 160 degrees, Fahrenheit.

In nearly all cases, however, the maximum water temperature you'll need for a radiant floor heating zone will be lower that the temperature you need for your convective hydronic zones and domestic hot water production. That means you'll have to find a way to get two or more separate temperatures out of the same boiler.

You'll also have to think about ways to protect your boiler from low-temperature return water. You don't want the flue gasses to condense inside the boiler or the flue, and you *certainly* don't want to run the risk of cracking the boiler through thermal shock.

If you're using a copper fin-tube boiler, the flow rate across the boiler's heat exchanger is also a very important consideration. If you don't maintain a certain minimum flow of water through these units, they'll shut off on high-temperature limit, or even produce steam!

There's a lot to consider when you work with multitemperature hydronic systems. The growing popularity of radiant floor heating is moving us in that direction, so let's take a look at a simple way to protect the boiler while getting exactly what you need for each zone.

Primary/Secondary Pumping

The simplest way to avoid boiler problems is to make sure there's always a supply of hot water blending into the cooler water that's returning from the system. That's what primary/secondary pumping does. And it does it in a very simple and inexpensive way.

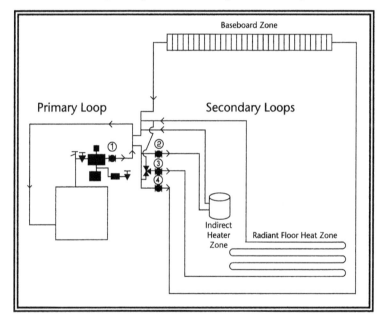

Here's a sketch of a system with three zones attached to a basic "pumping away" module. We have a low-temperature (120 degree) radiant floor heat zone, a high-temperature (180 degree) copper fin-tube base-board zone, and an indirect domestic hot water heater, which also needs 180-degree water.

Pump #1 is the primary pump. Its job is to make

sure that the temperature of the water returning to the boiler will always be higher than the point at which the flue gasses could begin to condense. If you're using a copper fin-tube boiler, the primary pump will also make sure you always have the proper flow of water moving through the boiler.

Pump #1 will run any time any of the zones call for heat. It will circulate hot boiler water past those two tees and back into the boiler. Any of the three secondary zone pumps can draw hot water out of the first tee, just as though the tee were the boiler. They'll return cooler water through the second tee where it will blend with the hot water Pump #1 is moving though the primary loop.

These two tees, and their location, are crucial to this system's operation.

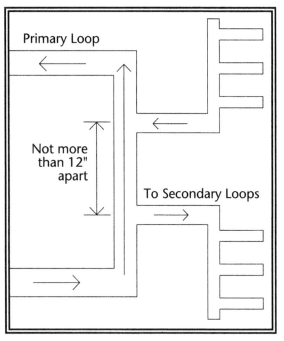

The trick is to pipe them very closely together, never more than a foot apart. Ideally, there should be about six-inches of space between them. When you pipe the tees this way, you'll be able to use pumps with different flow rates and head capabilities without having to worry that a large pump will overpower a smaller pump.

The principle at work in primary/secondary pumping is simple: water will *always* follow the path of least resistance. That means that when it enters a tee, it will always look for the easiest way out.

When Pump #1 is on, it will move its full flow of water around the primary loop. The primary loop, in this case, is the loop around the boiler.

The zone pumps (#2, #3, and #4) are the secondary pumps. When you set it up, make sure your secondary pumps always "pump away" from the supply tee and toward their zones. This is important because a secondary pump uses the common piping between the primary and secondary zones as its point of no pressure change, it's "compression tank," if you will. This is why in a primary/secondary system, even if its a multiple-boiler system, you still only have one *real* compression tank. The *real* tank will always be in the primary loop.

When you pump away from the common piping (the point of no pressure change), the secondary pump will add its differential pressure to the static fill pressure and you'll get all the benefits you get by pumping away from a real tank.

The secondary pumps, of course, can run either together or separately. How much hot water flows into the secondary circuits depends on how many secondary pumps come on. To make this a bit more visual, let's plug in some numbers.

Suppose you have a 140,000 Btuh boiler. To figure the flow rate you'll need for the boiler, just divide the Btuh load by a factor of 10,000 (the factor allows for a 20 degree temperature rise across the boiler).

$$\frac{140,000}{10,000} = 14 \text{ gpm}$$

Now, whenever the boiler is firing, you'll always

have 14 gpm zipping in and out of it, and passing between the two tees. Some, or all, of that water will flow out to the zones.

In this example, let's say the high-temperature (180 degree) baseboard zone need 30,000 Btuh at a 20-degree temperature drop. That means the water will enter the zone at 180 degrees, and leave it at 160 degrees. To figure the flow rate, just divide 30,000 Btuh by the factor 10,000. That gives you 3 gpm.

The low-temperature (120 degree) radiant floor heat zone also requires 30,000 Btuh at a 20-degree temperature drop. That's another 3 gpm, but in this case, it will return from the zone at 100 degrees.

So, all in all, you need a total flow rate of 6 gpm for space heating. The balance of the primary flow (8 gpm of 180 degree water) will go to the indirect water heater.

Okay, let's say the high-temperature baseboard zone calls for heat first. What happens?

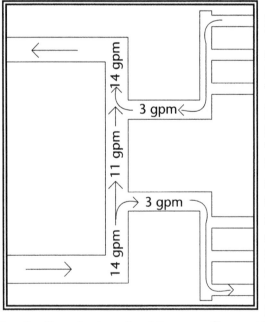

The primary pump delivers 14 gpm of 180-degree water to the first tee. The secondary pump draws 3 gpm of hot water out of the first tee, and at the same instant, returns 3 gpm of cooler water into the second tee. You now have 14 gpm flowing across the boiler, but only 11 gpm flows through the six inches of main between the two tees. The flow splits because the two pumps create a primary and a secondary path of least resistance.

Look at the sketch again. Can you see how the hot primary water raises the temperature of the water returning from the baseboard? If you're interested in finding out what the temperature will be, make yourself a simple sketch of the flow rates and temperatures.

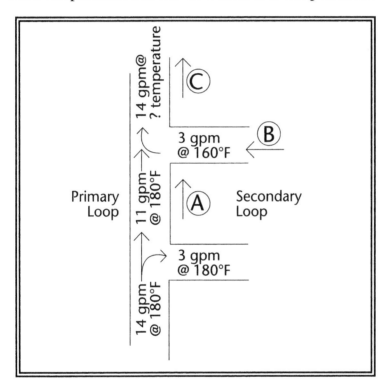

The ABC's of Return Temperature

To figure the boiler return temperature, you have to do a bit of math, but don't let that scare you, it's as easy as ABC. The formula works like this:

$$\frac{\overset{A}{\left(\substack{\text{Port A} \\ \text{Flow Rate}}\right)\left(\substack{\text{Port A} \\ \text{Temp.}}\right)} + \overset{B}{\left(\substack{\text{Port B} \\ \text{Flow Rate}}\right)\left(\substack{\text{Port B} \\ \text{Temp.}}\right)}}{\overset{C}{}}$$

$$= \left(\substack{\text{Port C} \\ \text{Flow Rate}}\right)\left(\substack{x \\ \text{degrees}}\right)$$

X-degrees, of course, is the boiler return temperature. To solve for it, just plug in the numbers. Remember to do your multiplying before you do your addition:

$$\overset{A}{\left(\substack{11 \\ \text{gpm}}\right)\left(\substack{180 \\ \text{degrees}}\right)} + \overset{B}{\left(\substack{3 \\ \text{gpm}}\right)\left(\substack{160 \\ \text{degrees}}\right)}$$

$$= \overset{C}{\left(\substack{14 \\ \text{gpm}}\right)}\left(\substack{X \\ \text{degrees}}\right)$$

So...

$$\overset{A}{(1980)} + \overset{B}{(480)} = \overset{C}{(14\,X)}$$

$$2460 = 14\,X$$

$$\frac{2460}{14} = \frac{14\,X}{14}$$

$$X = 175.7$$

So the water flowing back to the boiler will be 175.7 degrees when the baseboard zone calls for heat. The end result hardly seems worth the effort because even without the primary pump, the water leaving the baseboard zone would be 160 degrees. At that temperature, there's no chance it's going to shock your boiler or condense the flue gasses. By mixing hot boiler water into it, you've raised its temperature to nearly what it was when it left the boiler.

But consider what might happen when 90- or 100-degree water returns from the radiant floor heat zone. Unless you raise the temperature of **this** water by blending hot boiler water into it, you can run the risk of damaging the boiler or the flue.

Let's see how that works out. We're returning 3 gpm of 100 degree water to the primary loop. Plug in the numbers:

$$\underset{A}{\left(\frac{11}{\text{gpm}}\right)\left(\frac{180}{\text{degrees}}\right)} + \underset{B}{\left(\frac{3}{\text{gpm}}\right)\left(\frac{100}{\text{degrees}}\right)}$$

$$= \underset{C}{\left(\frac{14}{\text{gpm}}\right)}\left(\frac{X}{\text{degrees}}\right)$$

So...

$$\underset{A}{(1980)} + \underset{B}{(300)} = \underset{C}{(14\,X)}$$

$$2280 = 14\,X$$

$$\frac{2280}{14} = \frac{14\,X}{14}$$

$$X = 162.8$$

So even though the radiant floor heat zone returns 100 water, the boiler never sees a temperature lower than 162.8 degrees, and if you're using a copper fin-tube boiler, the flow rate will also be correct. Not bad.

Can you see how the simplicity of primary/secondary pumping protects you against all potential flow and temperature problems? Sure, you need that additional pump and a bit more piping to do it this way, but the benefits you get **more** than justify the added expense. Pumps are cheaper than boilers. In fact, some boiler manufacturers are now supplying the primary pump as a part of their package. It's there to simplify operation and to prolong the boiler's life.

Not bad at all!

How To Size Your Piping

To size primary/secondary piping, make sure you consider the combined flow you'll need at any given point.

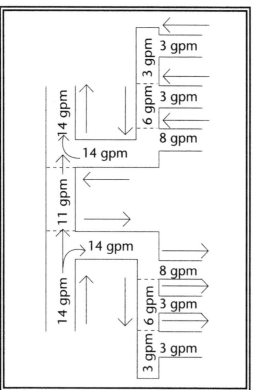

For instance, in our example, the primary loop has to handle 14 gpm. The secondary loops handle 3 gpm, 3 gpm and 8 gpm, respectively. What size pipe do you need for those flow rates?

Here are a couple of charts that will help you find the:

Maximum, Trouble-Free Design Flow Rates For Hot Water Heating:

Copper Pipe

$1/2$"	$1^1/2$ gpm
$3/4$"	4 gpm
1"	8 gpm
$1^1/4$"	14 gpm
$1^1/2$"	22 gpm
2"	45 gpm
$2^1/2$"	85 gpm
3"	130 gpm

Steel Pipe

$1/2$"	2 gpm
$3/4$"	4 gpm
1"	8 gpm
$1^1/4$"	16 gpm
$1^1/2$"	25 gpm
2"	50 gpm
$2^1/2$"	80 gpm
3"	140 gpm
4"	300 gpm

On this job, you need 14 gpm in the primary loop. That means you'll use $1^1/4$" pipe (copper or steel, your choice). Your tees will also be $1^1/4$".

The flow potential through the secondary supply and return manifolds gets a bit more interesting. You could see any of these conditions:

3 gpm (if one space-heating zone calls)
6 gpm (if both space-heating zones call at the same time)
8 gpm (if the indirect heater calls)
11 gpm (if a space-heating zone *and* the indirect

heater call)
14 gpm (if all zones call at the same time).

To keep things simple, you can size the supply and return manifolds for the greatest possible flow (14 gpm, in this case). Or, if you want, you can reduce the manifold size as you shed load to the zones. The return manifold, of course, will see the same flow, only in reverse.

In this example, it pays to make the indirect heater the first take-off from the supply manifold because it has the largest flow rate.

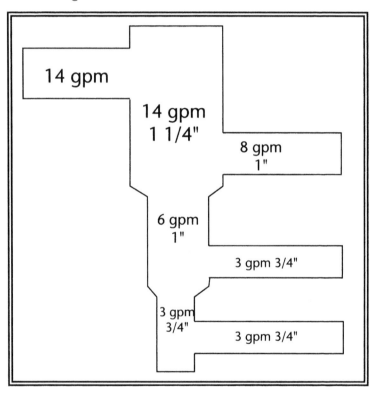

You need to use 1¼" pipe all the way up to the indirect heater because the flow to that point will be 14 gpm when all the zones call at the same time. Since you're sending 8 gpm to the heater, branch off with a 1" line, and then reduce the manifold to 1" as well. That's the right size because the maximum flow beyond the take-off to the heater will only be 6 gpm.

Branch off the 1" line with 3/4" to send 3 gpm into the next zone, and reduce the main to 3/4" as well to feed the next zone with the final 3 gpm.

You can use the rule-of-thumb charts to figure out what size manifold you'll need for any job. Just think your way through the system and ask yourself where you would flow if you were the water. Then, accommodate it with the right size pipe.

As I said, the return manifold will be the mirror image of the supply manifold because it's picking up the same flow the supply manifold just dropped off.

No matter how you choose to pipe your manifold, it pays to make your take-offs to the zones from the **bottom** instead of from the top of the manifold. This simple trick can help you avoid a particularly nagging type of air problem.

Here's what I mean. There will be times when, say, only 3 gpm flows through a manifold that's capable of handling 14 gpm. When this happens, the manifold pretend it's an air separator.

You see, anytime the water's velocity slows to less than six inches per second, entrained air can separate out of the water and gather at the top of the pipe. The air released from the flow of the "on" zone can float up into an "off" zone when the water passes through the manifold. Just like this.

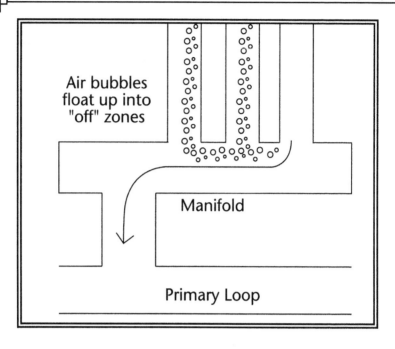

Those bubbles are off into another zone before the system's air separator has a chance to catch them. By making your zone connections from the **bottom** instead of the top of the manifold, the air won't float away. Instead, it will continue into the primary loop where the air separator can deal with it.

Remember, **every** hydronic system should have a good air separator in the common supply piping. The separator will continuously remove any air from the water as it passes through and greatly improve the system's performance. Automatic air vents stuck into the piping at random can't rid the system of air because the water's passing by too fast. You have to slow the water down to catch the air. That's what air separators specialize in.

Now let's take a look at a few ways you can lower the temperature of the water before it enters the secondary zone.

Radiant Floor Heating With A 3-Way Valve

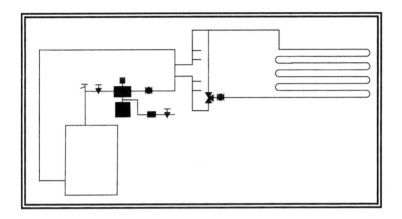

Here, you're using a self-contained 3-way valve to blend the relatively cool water that's returning from the zone back into the hot water that's leaving the boiler. The valve works as a temperature limiter. You set it to the maximum temperature you'll need on the coldest day of the year (whoever sizes the radiant floor heat zone decides that temperature). The circulator cycles on and off at the call of a room thermostat, or a slab-temperature sensor (these are great for radiant floor heat systems in sun rooms).

You can also use this piping strategy to add a radiant floor heat zone to an existing hydronic system if you'd like. It's simple and relatively inexpensive.

A friend of mine recently remodeled a second-floor bathroom in a house that had a two-zone loop system. He removed the copper fin-tube baseboard that served the old bathroom and installed a small water-lubricated circulator and a 3-way valve inside the new vanity. The vanity also hid the radiant floor heat manifolds.

It looked like this.

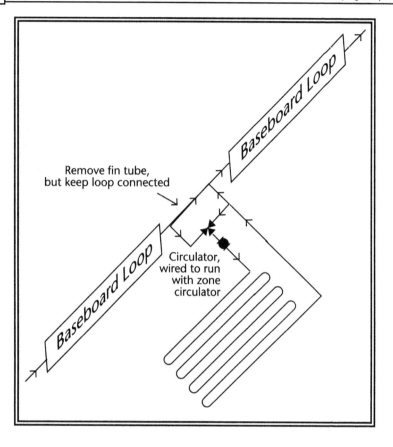

He set the 3-way valve to deliver a maximum of 120 degree water to the radiant floor heat tubing he'd installed under the new tile floor and behind the tiled walls, and then he wired the new circulator so it would run at the same time as the zone circulator. It wasn't an independent zone, but it worked beautifully, and the customer loves his warm tiles.

If you want to better track the temperature in a radiant floor heat zone, you can use a 3-way valve with a reset controller.

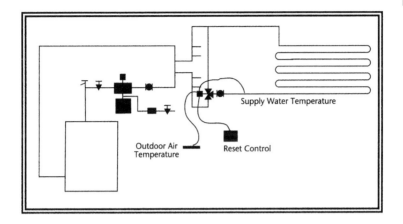

Here, you're sensing outdoor air temperature and the temperature of the water going to (or in some cases, coming from) the zone. The circulator operates continuously whenever the outdoor temperature drops below a preset point. With constant flow, and variable temperature, you're able to input the *exact* amount of heat you need at any given moment.

This is a fine way to get the job done, but the valve and reset control *does* cost more than a simple, self-contained 3-way valve. The drawback with the self-contained valve, of course, is that you're always supplying the zone with the *maximum* temperature. You can't match the heat input to the varying heat loss. A self-contained 3-way valve is not as good as a reset system, but it *is* less expensive.

Not sure what to do? A good rule of thumb for radiant floor heating systems is that the controls shouldn't cost more than the tubing. In other words, the larger the job (where there's *lots* of tubing), the more likely you'll be to benefit by using a reset controller. However, if you're just adding a warm floor to a remodeled bathroom (where there's not much tubing), you can be very successful with a simpler system.

In other words, you can add enough sophistication and expense to the job to make just about *any* customer change his mind. Examine your options, and find a sensible balance.

To keep costs to an absolute minimum, some installers use a 3-way ball valve or a simple boiler-bypass line with two balancing valves instead of a temperature-sensitive 3-way valve.

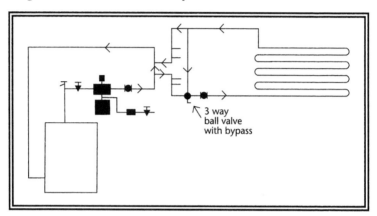

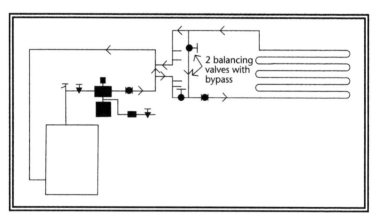

You adjust the 3-way ball valve or the balancing valves to mix the water returning from the system back into the hot boiler water. Once you reach the proper setting, you take the handles off the valve to prevent tampering.

This system can work, but it's *very* crude. You're relying on the flow rate and boiler temperature to remain fairly constant - and usually, that's asking for a lot.

Which brings me to a story.

Right after World War II, William Levitt mass-produced 50,000 homes in New York and Pennsylvania. He called these communities Levittown. None of the Levittown homes had basements. All of them sat on concrete slabs. Levitt heated these homes with under-floor radiant systems. He embedded soft cooper pipe in the concrete slab of each house and placed the boiler in the kitchen.

The boiler had a tankless coil to make domestic hot water so it had to maintain 180 degree temperature all the time. The radiant floor heating system, however, needed only 120 degree supply water. Levitt managed the two temperatures by using a ³/₄" boiler bypass line at the outlet side of the circulator, and a ³/₄" X ¹/₈" bushing between the bypass and the boiler. It looked like this.

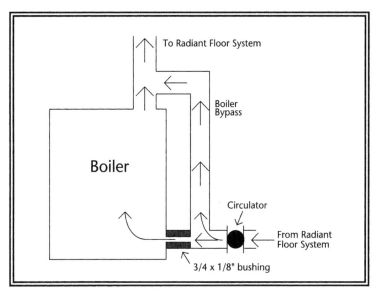

Keep in mind, these homes had only one heating zone - the radiant floor system. Most of the water returning from the zone would bypass the boiler and head right back into the floor. Only the water that could fit through the 1/8" hole in the return line bushing would enter the boiler. An equal amount of hot water would, at the same time, blend into the bypassing return water, raising its temperature as it flowed back toward the buried copper tubing.

As time went by, these tankless coils fouled. The home owners would call for service and, rather than clean the coil, the service technician would simply raise the high-limit aquastat to about 210 degrees. That certainly gave the folks more domestic hot water!

The trouble was, when the serviceman raised the temperature of the water in the boiler, he also raised the temperature of the water flowing through the floor. That wasn't his intention, but because of the crude nature of the system, that's what he got.

Before long, the floor got so hot, the people couldn't stand on it. The dog wouldn't get off the couch. The cat wouldn't get off the chandelier. The floor tiles in the kitchen came lose and slid around like hockey pucks.

But they sure had plenty of domestic hot water.

This is the problem with using a manual 3-way valve or a simple bypass to control a radiant floor heat zone. If you have more than one zone, and you're not using primary-secondary pumping techniques, the flow and temperature through your radiant floor heat zone can change as other pumps start and stop. You might not be happy with the results.

So consider this method *only* as a last resort.

Radiant Floor Heating With A 2-Way Valve

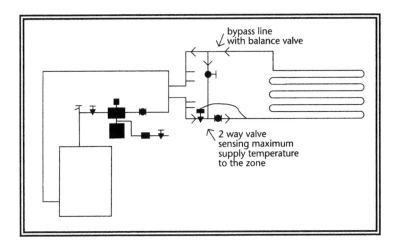

bypass line with balance valve

2 way valve sensing maximum supply temperature to the zone

This is another way to get the job done without spending a lot of money. You'll use a self-contained 2-way valve to control the **maximum** temperature allowed into the radiant floor heat zone.

The 2-way valve is similar to the thermostatic radiator valves we looked at before (made by the same folks, in fact), but here, the operator senses the temperature of the supply water to the zone, not the temperature of the air in the room. The 2-way valve closes on a rise in temperature.

When you're working with a two-temperature system, the zone pump will *always* be on the tubing side of the temperature-control valve. That's so it can mix return water back into supply water. In this system, the pump cycles on and off at the call of the room thermostat. That bypass line you see between the 2-way valve and the suction side of the pump allows a portion of the return water to flow through and join with the hot water from the boiler. How much water flows through the bypass line depends on how wide open the

2-way valve is at any moment. You use the bypass balance valve to fine-tune the temperature.

Take a minute to trace the water's flow options through the system, keeping in mind that the water flowing into the radiant floor heat zone will never be hotter than the temperature you've set at the 2-way valve.

Two-way valves usually offer less resistance to flow than do 3-way valves. Three-way valves have a throttling piston that opens the cold port at the same time it's closing the hot port. That's how it finds the right temperature.

But because of the 3-way valve's close internal tolerances, they're fairly susceptible to system debris and any sludge that may develop as time goes by. Two-way valves are less likely to get stuck because they open and close only one port. If you visualize a motorized globe valve, you'll have a good idea of how they work. They're very simple in operation and are well worth considering.

You can also adapt the 2-way valve system to a reset controller.

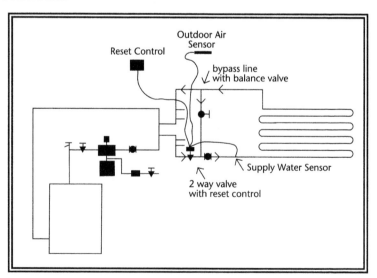

This system works basically the same way. The only difference is that the 2-way valve will now sense both outdoor-air temperature **and** supply water temperature. It will be able to match the input to the heat loss perfectly on any day of the year. The supply water temperature will automatically drift up and down along a reset curve, getting hotter when the day gets colder, and cooler when the day gets hotter.

Here again, consider the rule of thumb: The controls shouldn't cost more than the tubing.

Radiant Floor Heating With A 4-Way Valve

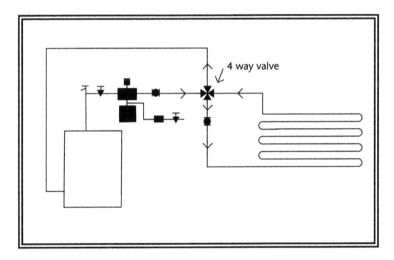

Another way to protect your boiler against low-temperature return water or a low-flow condition is to use a 4-way valve. The 4-way valve replaces the supply and return tees you used in the primary/secondary system we looked at before.

You still have two circulators, one for the boiler, and one for the zone, so it *is* similar to primary/secondary. But now, instead of supplying hot water to a manifold that serves both high- *and* low-temperature zones, you're serving only one, low-temperature zone.

A 4-way valve has an inlet and an outlet for the boiler, and an inlet and an outlet for the low-temperature zone. Its design pretty much guarantees you'll *never* return cold water to the boiler.

Let's take a closer look inside one.

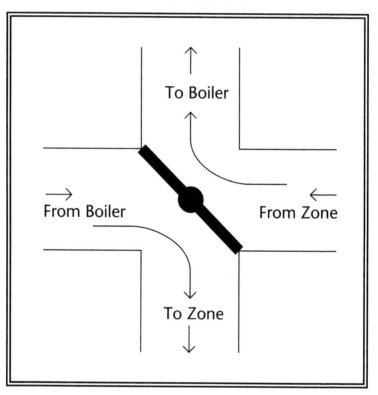

Water flows either to the boiler or to the zone. It all depends on the position of the internal paddle. The paddle is connected to the valve's stem. As you see it in the drawing, right now the valve is wide open with all of the boiler water flowing out to the zone.

You can control the position of the paddle by either setting it by hand for a fixed, maximum-temperature condition, or by connecting it to a reset controller so the system can track the outside air temperature and modulate the supply water temperature to the zone.

Here's what the valve looks like when it's throttling.

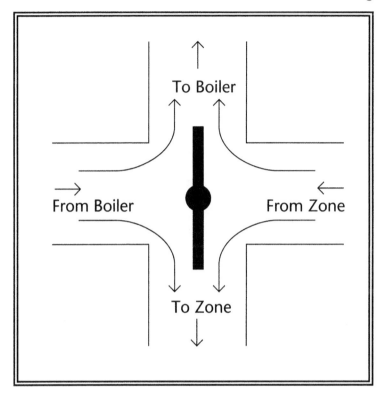

Some of the hot water flows from the boiler into the zone while the balance of the water returns directly to the boiler. On the low-temperature side, some of the water flows back to the boiler, as the rest returns to the zone.

When the valve throttles like this, hot boiler water will always mix with cool return water. This protects the boiler from thermal shock and condensing flue gasses. If you have a copper fin-tube boiler, a 4-way valve will make sure there's a constant flow of water through the boiler. This keeps the boiler from shutting down on high-temperature.

If you're using a reset controller, there are going to be times whcn the valve is in this position.

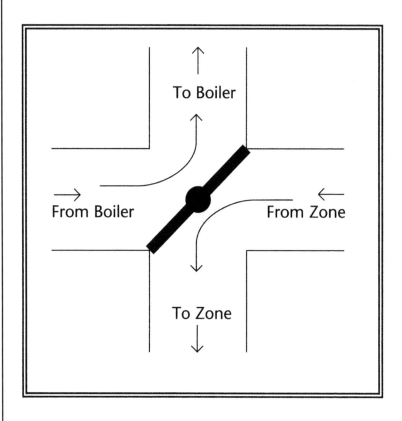

This will happen on a mild day when the radiant floor heat zone doesn't need to take much heat out of the water. The zone water circulates continuously through the zone without passing through the boiler. On the boiler side, the water continues to move through the boiler, making itself available to other zones.

Radiant Floor Heat With A Variable-Speed, Heat Injection Pump

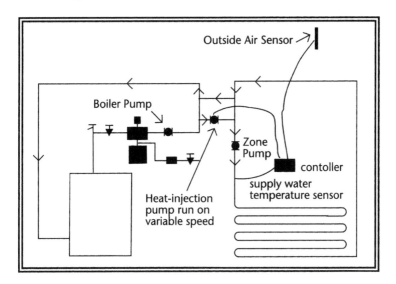

In this system, a special controller runs a small wet-rotor circulator on variable speed to inject hot water into the continuously flowing radiant floor heat zone. The controller senses the supply water temperature and the outdoor air temperature and bleeds in just the right amount of heated water to match the zone's needs on any given day. Since the pump is running on variable speed, it's able to fine tune the temperature without over-shooting the mark.

The control (introduced by tekmar Control Systems in early-1994) replaces the 4-way valve with an inexpensive, run-of-the-mill circulator and achieves the same goal: to protect the boiler against low temperature, and to supply the zone with the exact amount of heat it needs.

This control scheme involves a bit more piping, but there's nothing at all complicated about it. It's well worth looking into.

Multiple-Boiler Systems

Now let's move back to primary/secondary pumping again and see how you can use these same techniques to build a multiple-boiler system. But first, let me give you a few reasons why you'd want to build a multiple-boiler system in the first place:

1. Every day is not the coldest day of the year. In fact, the "coldest day of the year," probably isn't even a full day! You may see the design temperature for only a few hours out of the entire year. With a multiple-boiler system, you can split the load into several boilers and only fire a part of the total load on days when it's not that cold outside. Multiple-boiler systems save fuel.

2. You get to use smaller boilers that are easy to move around. This is especially important on retrofit work where they may have installed the original boiler, and then built the building on top of it. Smaller boilers are also easier to install. Multiple-boiler systems often save time and money.

3. You get built-in stand-by capability with a multiple-boiler system. If one boiler goes down, you always have another boiler (or two or three) you can call on. Your customer will probably never be without heat and hot water when you give him a multiple-boiler system. Multiple-boiler systems provide security.

4. Not everyone has the capability, the help,

or even the tools needed to install large boilers. Multiple-boiler systems open up a world of commercial possibilities to heating contractors who have previously only tackled residential work.

5. By using primary/secondary pumping, you won't have any water flowing through a boiler that's not firing. This cuts stand-by losses and saves fuel. Multiple-boiler systems make sense.

Here's one way you can pipe a primary/secondary, multiple-boiler system.

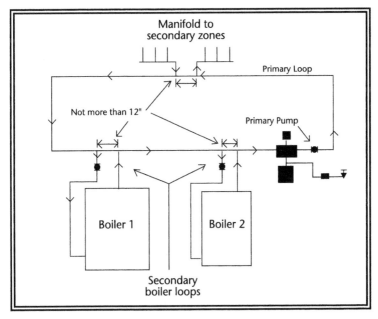

At first glance, it looks a bit complicated, but it's really not. The primary pump is the one that's pumping the boiler-room loop. The secondary pumps are either serving the boilers, or sending water out to the zones (the zone pumps are just like the ones we looked at before).

The primary pump just moves water around the boiler room. It flows back and forth between the tees connecting the boilers and the two tees that lead to the secondary zones. This primary pump is usually a small one, designed to move a flow equal to the system's Btuh capacity, but at a *very* low head pressure (just look at how short the loop is!).

The boiler pump comes on with the burner to move hot water up into the primary loop. It, too, is usually a very small pump because it's only concerned with the flow needs of the one boiler, and the head needs of its small loop.

The primary pump receives the heated water from the boiler pump and sends it around the primary loop where it becomes available to the secondary, zone pumps. They, in turn, draw heated water out of the supply tee and instantly replace what they removed with a rush of cooler return water into the return tee. The return water blends with the primary flow and continues around the loop.

On very cold days, both boilers (and their secondary pumps) come on. The primary-loop water now flows through both boilers, picking up heat as it goes. On mild days, it flows though only one boiler, picking up less heat. Naturally, you can split the total load even further by adding additional boilers.

Notice, too, how all the secondary pumps, whether they're serving the boilers or the zones, are all **pumping away** from the point of no pressure change. There's only one compression tank. The primary pump uses it as *its* point of no pressure change. The secondary pumps use the common piping between the primary and secondary loops as *their* points of no pressure change.

To simplify piping on larger jobs, you can run the primary loop around the perimeter of the building in a drop ceiling. Just like this.

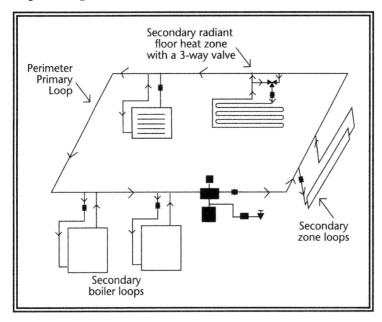

The first thing you'd install on this job would be the primary loop. Insulate it well. Then, once the walls start going up, you can cut into the insulation and "hang" your radiation and boilers from the suspended loop.

A good way to control these systems is to use a reset controller to operate the primary pump, the secondary boiler pumps and the burners. The primary pump comes on when the outdoor temperature drops to a preset point. The secondary boiler pumps come on with the burners to raise the primary-loop temperature to whatever is needed at the moment. The boiler control can be a simple high-limit aquastat; the reset control will tell it how long to run.

The secondary zone pumps come on at the call of a thermostat to draw water down off the primary loop.

In all cases, the space between the tees that connect any secondary loop to the primary loop should never be more than 12″. By keeping the tees this close, you can have pumps of different sizes within the same system without having the larger ones overpowering the smaller ones. In addition, you won't have to use flow-control valves at the secondary zones because no water will flow into them when their little pumps are off (Remember, the zones are lower than the main).

To size your primary and secondary piping, you can follow the same rule of thumb we talked about before:

Based on a 20-degree temperature drop, one gallon per minute of flow will transport 10,000 Btuh.

So, for instance, if you were trying to move 500,000 Btuh at a 20-degree temperature drop around a primary loop, you'd just divide by the factor 10,000 to get 50 gpm:

$$\frac{500{,}000}{10{,}000} = 50 \text{ gpm}$$

And here again are those flow-rate/pipe size rules of thumb we looked at earlier:

Maximum, Trouble-Free Design Flow Rates For Hot Water Heating:

Copper Pipe

1/2″	1 1/2 gpm
3/4″	4 gpm
1″	8 gpm
1 1/4″	14 gpm
1 1/2″	22 gpm

2"	45 gpm
2¹/₂"	85 gpm
3"	130 gpm

Steel Pipe

¹/₂"	2 gpm
³/₄"	4 gpm
1"	8 gpm
1¹/₄"	16 gpm
1¹/₂"	25 gpm
2"	50 gpm
2¹/₂"	80 gpm
3"	140 gpm
4"	300 gpm

Think carefully, and then size your pipe for the amount of water you need to move through any part of the system. The primary loop needs all the water, the boiler secondary loops need to flow only what the individual boilers need (Btuh divided by 10,000 = gpm). The same goes for the radiation zones. Size the pumps for the load you're moving through that particular loop, no more and no less.

As for pump head, a good rule of thumb is to allow six feet of head for each 100 feet of piping. This takes into consideration the additional pressure drop created by the fittings, valves and hydronic specialties.

So, for instance, let's say you need to move 20 gpm (200,000 Btuh) through a primary loop that runs for a total of 200 feet. First, look at the pipe sizing chart. You'll need 1¹/₂" pipe to accommodate 20 gpm. Next, allow 6 feet of pump head for each 100 feet of piping in your loop. That gives you 12 feet. Finally, select a primary pump to move 20 gpm against a head of 12 feet. Easy!

Select your secondary pumps the same way - for the

flow you need in that particular zone at the head they need to produce. And keep in mind when you're figuring pump head, you don't have to measure *all* the piping in the building, just the loop the pump serves.

You'll almost always wind up with small, in-line pumps on both the primary and secondary loops. They're inexpensive, easy to find, and easy to replace when the time comes.

Be an Imagineer

If you were water, which way would you go? If you were air, could you get out? What does a Btu look like? How big is it? If you could hold it in your hand, what would it feel like? How much would it weigh? What color is it?

These are some of the questions Imagineers ask themselves. Imagineers like to pretend they're inside the pipes, riding the water in a rubber boat. When they're troubleshooting, they take a mental walk through the system and think like water and air. Which way would *I* go if I were the water? If I were air, could I get out of here?

Imagineers think in simple terms. They look at **systems**, not just symptoms, and they take things one step at a time. They're very effective troubleshooters because they take the time to think, *really think*, about what's going on. And they fully define the problem before trying to solve it. And they have fun.

They consider the color and the weight and the texture of British Thermal Units and other things that don't exist because they know there will be days when they'll have to explain invisible things such as these to people who know *nothing* about heating, but who might buy something from them - if only the Imagineer can make them *see* what's going on.

An Imagineer might light a match and let it burn

until it reaches the very tip of his finger. The customer will watch, sitting on the edge of his seat. "That's a single Btu," the Imagineer will say. "When your burner comes on, it will be like 7,500 **books** of matches, all flaring up at the same instant. Imagine that power!"

Imagineers paint word pictures. People love word pictures.

A clever Imagineer might say, "The Btus ride the water like a passenger on a train. They get on in the boiler and off in the radiators. I size the pipe properly so all the passengers can fit on the train." The home owner nods his head in understanding.

When discussing a radiant floor heating system, an Imagineer talks about supermarkets and freezers and the human body as a radiator - things people can wrap their minds around. A good Imagineer never forgets that people don't buy boilers and pumps and valves and controls. They buy **_comfort_**. They buy what this stuff *does*, not what it *is*. Can you see that?

People buy things that are as intangible as a Btu, and as screwy as a pet rock.

So think a little bit every day. Do it in the bathroom. The bathroom is inspirational! Let the hot water beat down on your head, and don't talk to anyone, or listen to the radio. Just think!

Do it every day. It adds up, with interest.

And get enthusiastic. Enthusiasm is positively contagious. Always remember, there are no boring subjects, there are only boring people.

I once met a man who was passionate about ice because that's what he sold. Ice fed his family. He talked to me about clarity and the lack of bubbles in his ice. He explained how his packaging kept his ice from dripping all over your car. He talked about the size and shape of cubes and how his fit through the narrow neck of sports bottles. The guy was passionate about ice. He waved his arms around and smiled a crazy grin -

just like Gil Carlson used to do in those days I remember so well.

The ice man made me see the magic. So did Gil Carlson.

There are **_no_** boring subjects, there are only boring people who hate their jobs. And boring people are as contagious as enthusiastic people. You can catch one or the other just as easily. It's all up to you, bub.

So think a little bit every day about the way you spend your working hours, and why you do things the way you do them. Think about the Dead Men who came before you, and give yourself a half-hour every weekend to think about the business you're *really* in.

Use your imagination, it's a precious gift from God. Remember how fertile that imagination was when you were a little kid. Strive to bring it back to that same level. It takes practice, but boy it's fun!

Do this now: Think about what a British Thermal Unit looks like, how big it is, what is feels like, how much it weighs, what color it is. And when you've got it all figured out, go describe it to some little kid. Don't stop describing until you make her see that Btu in her mind's eye. Make that kid smile with delight.

Then go talk to the people. They'll hear the pictures in your head, and they'll buy what you're selling: ***Comfort!***

Index

Airtrol Tank Fitting (Bell & Gossett's), 54-55, 58

Air problems (caused by return manifold), 95-96

Air separators:
Built-in-type, 56-60
scoop-type, 49
orifice-type, 49
micro-bubbler reabsorber-type, 49

Balancing fittings, 70

Baseboard radiation, 66-67, 74-75

Bell & Gossett, 2

Boyle, Robert, 19

Boyle's Law of Perfect Gasses, 19-21

Calc-Plus software, 67

Carbon-dioxide, 33

Carlson, Gil, 2, 5, 7-8, 118

Centrifugal force, 25-26

Ceramics, 8

Circulators, 22-32

Coal heat, 5

Coal stoves, 5

"Cold 70", 82-83

Compression tank (diaphragm) 14-18, 40, 49, 59, 87

Compression tank (steel) 7-10, 21, 52-56, 58
How air leaves, 54
Proper fill level, 56

Convection, 82, 83

Cv, 76-77

Differential-pressure valves, 72-75

Diverter-tee system, 7, 51-52, 75-77

Eisenhower, Dwight David, 5

Evaporation, 81

Feed valves, 22, 38-41

Four-way valves, 105-108

Forced hot air, 6

Friction loss, 12

Gravity furnaces, 5

Gravity hot water heat, 5

Henry's Law, 32-34

Imagineering, 116-118

Impellers, 25-26

IAS air separator
(Bell & Gossett's), 53

Levitt, William, 101

Levittown, 101

Mechanical seals (pumps)
6-7

Multiple-Boiler systems,
110-116

One-pipe, baseboard loop
systems, 66-67

One-pipe, diverter-tee
systems, 67-69

Oxygen corrosion, 7

Packaged boilers, 5, 9

Pipe sizing rules of
thumb, 93, 114-115

Point of no pressure
change, 3, 10, 12, 34-46

Pressure differential, 24,
28-32, 34-37

Primary\Secondary
pumping, 85-96

pipe sizing for, 92-96

with multiple-boiler
systems, 111-116

with variable-speed,
heat-injection pump,
109

Pump curve, 24, 31

Pump head pressure,
11-12

"Pumping Away" piping,
48-52

"Heating Module", 61

Purging (of system air),
49-52

Radiant floor-heating
systems:

post-World War II
systems, 101-102

piping off existing
baseboard, 97-98

principle of operation,
81-85

relative cost of
operation, 82

with bypass bushing,
101

with four-way valves,
105-108

with three-way ball
valves, 100

with two balancing
valves, 100

with self-contained three-way valves, 97-100

with self-contained two-way valves, 103-104

with reset two-way valves, 104

with reset three-way valves, 99

within a primary\ secondary system, 85

how to predict boiler return temperature, 86-92

Radiation, 82

Reset systems, 79-81, 99

Slant/Fin, 67

Steam heat, 5, 6

Suburbs, 5

tekmar Control Systems, 109

Thermostatic radiator valves:

on two-pipe systems, 71-74

on one-pipe systems, 74-77

Three-way valves, 97-100

Total dynamic head, 23

Two-pipe, direct-return systems, 69-71, 78

Two-pipe, reverse-return systems, 77-79

United States Radiator Corp. 4

Wood heat, 5

World War II, 5, 101

9 780974 396088